11-3-49
2-27-50

BOBWHITES ON THE RISE

BOBWHITES
ON THE RISE

BY

VERNE E. DAVISON

WITH ILLUSTRATIONS BY
WALLACE HUGHES

CHARLES SCRIBNER'S SONS, NEW YORK
CHARLES SCRIBNER'S SONS, LTD., LONDON

1949

DEDICATED

To Those Who Hunt the Bobwhite Quail

AND

To the Landowners, Who Alone Can Grow

More of Them

662675

PREFACE

"Bobwhites on the Rise" presents the concept of Land Management as the chief influence on the welfare and production of the bobwhite quail. Too much reliance has been placed upon nature and man-made laws which were expected to conserve and increase the number of the coveted, popular bobwhites. Not enough attention has been given to the lands where food and cover can be provided. Conservation, alone, is not enough. This book turns the spotlight on agriculture, particularly to the wildlife-lands upon which essential practices may be applied in economically-sound farm patterns.

Quail management is dependent on hundreds-of-thousands of landholders. To give workable directions to these people "Bobwhites on the Rise" was written. It contains the essential information for quail management and approaches the problem with simple practices—easily understood by the farmer, preserve owner, absentee farmer, and hunter.

Preparation and completion of this book was made possible by the kindly, pertinent suggestions and editorial assistance of Dr. Edward H. Graham, Chief, Biology Division, Soil Conservation Service; Gordon Webb, Information Division, Soil Conservation Service; and my wife, Mildred. I have not forgotten the inestimable help afforded me by my friends and associates throughout my 45 years. They are simply too numerous to recount—they include particularly the field technicians and administrators of the Soil Conservation Service, and many of the employees of state game departments and the Fish and Wildlife Service. Many were private citizens who own and manage land to favor the bobwhites.

VERNE E. DAVISON

Spartanburg, S. C.
June, 1949

TABLE OF CONTENTS

CHAPTER I
BOBWHITE AND ITS RANGE

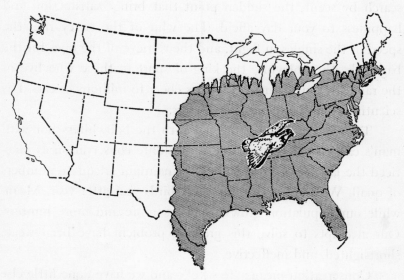

Of all the game birds in America, the bobwhite quail is the most popular. He has never been charged with any kind of destructiveness. He is heralded as a bird totally beneficial to human society throughout his extensive range. Bobwhite is an insectivorous bird, songbird, small-game, farm-game, and is the pride of many hunting preserves. He is a friend of the farmer, the hunter, and the bird lover.

Unfortunately there are not enough bobwhites. No hunter finds enough to hunt. No farm or ranch or timber tract supports as many birds as the owner and his friends would like. Fortunately, however, the number of bobwhites can be increased throughout their vast range in North America.

1

To the hunter nothing rivals the sport of a day afield with his bird dog in pursuit of the little birds known more affectionately as "partridges" or just plain "birds." It's the beauty of the bird dog's work; the first signs of him "makin' game"; the careful search by scent; the sudden point that brings satisfaction and happiness to your day afield. The whir of the covey rise, the speed of the singles in flight, and the retrieve of the ones for the bag make the bobwhite the king of sport to those who live in the range. His whistling call brings cheer to millions of ears. His scientific name is *Colinus virginianus*.

To our regret all is not well with the bobwhites—nor with man's care of the land for them! Wildlife conservation as practiced the last 25 years has failed to maintain adequate numbers of quail. We have fewer and fewer birds year after year. Meanwhile our population grows; we have more and more hunters. Our attempts to solve this growing problem have been weak, shortsighted, and ineffective.

Conservation means "to save"—and we have done little else than try to save birds from a steady exhaustion in numbers. Conservation is not enough! We must either resort to production for more birds or resign ourselves to a still lower bird population.

The decision is not up to the American sportsmen alone, as many people might believe. It will be a joint determination made by those who own the land and those who hunt the birds. Twenty-five years from now no one will have good quail hunting except: (1) the man who owns the land, (2) his friends whom he invites to hunt, or (3) the men who pay some landowner to produce for them a huntable surplus of quail. Most of us will admit that this inevitable day is not far off. It has already become a sad reality to the great majority of would-be hunters.

If you want to understand the bird and the problems of his production, you must know something of his entire range. You should know the heart and fringes of the range where the problems of management are different. Quail management is a serious business, requiring intelligent care of the land to feed and protect the coveys. But, alas, we have talked of these things in many tongues because our literature has dealt with local problems. Many have thought the same conditions exist significantly all over the bobwhite range. A student in Wisconsin is right when he says "Cover is the greatest need." So is the South Carolinian who lives on the coast and contends "food is our major requirement." And when we think of food, again we must think of that part of the range in which we wish to grow it. A few moments to consider the range will locate our problems geographically.

THE NATURAL RANGE OF THE BOBWHITE

East of the north-and-south line cutting the United States in half lies the range of the bobwhite quail. The range is bounded on the west by the semi-arid Great Plains; on the south by the Gulf of Mexico; on the east by the Atlantic Ocean; and on the north by an indefinite barrier of low winter temperatures, running across our northern states and southern Ontario, Canada. Except for a few counties in Canada and a part of two small states in northeastern Mexico, the bobwhite range lies within the United States.

For practical purposes there is only one kind of bobwhite. Peninsular Florida has a subspecies slightly smaller and dark colored, known as "Florida bobwhite" (*Colinus virginianus floridanus*). Texas and Mexico have a similar bird but lighter in color (as species in arid country often are) called "Texas bobwhite"

(*Colinus virginianus texanus*). Other subspecies are less distinct and may not deserve separation. Since trapping and restocking have become recognized as only gestures in conservation, the different subspecies are of no importance to the hunter or the game manager. To the ornithologist, the variations are obviously interesting; but these differences are discussed in other books dealing with classifications of species and subspecies.

THE NORTHERN FRINGE

Bobwhites are adapted to temperate zones, reaching greater abundance commonly in the southern states where the rigors of winter are relatively mild. Somewhere to the north the wintry storms are too severe even in the mildest years. This is beyond the fringe. Like giant icicles the frozen North frequently stabs with jagged ruthlessness into the more exposed lands of the northern states. At such times (the coldest winters or the worst storms) quail die by freezing or starvation or a combination of both. In average and more favorable years, the bobwhite holds his own or builds up in population. So in a broad sense there is a belt across our northern states where life for the bobwhites is a hazardous uncertainty, where they will be hard hit when the killer-storms occur.

Actually the belt is irregular at the edge. It darts northward with the protective shelter of major streams and their tributaries; the southern slopes are warmer than the shaded sides of the north. The area is dotted by thousands of coverts which in varying degree hold back the killing pressures of the storms. A man may strengthen his barriers which protect his quail, and he may assure them plenteous food by thoughtful care; but the fields of the northern fringe are dangerous homes for the bobwhite quail. Thus, cover against the cold and snows becomes the number one need in the north.

From the standpoint of shootable numbers, a state or a county in the northern fringe will do well to recognize the character of its handicaps. It is not likely that an abundance of bobwhites can be attained in the coldest belt of the range.

Durward Allen (1941) referring to the effect of winter weather on northern bobwhites makes several statements worth your knowing. "Although bobwhites might be very plentiful and afford good shooting for several years (in Michigan), hard winters sometimes wiped them out over large areas or reduced their numbers so drastically that it took as much as a decade for them to become reestablished. It is quite evident that in the bobwhite quail we have a species whose distribution to the north is delimited by climate.

"Snow may cause mortality in several ways. As it piles up in depth over weed seeds and grains, or when accompanied by low temperatures and high wind, it may bury a covey completely and imprison them in a cell where they die either from starvation or suffocation.

"It seems justifiable," he concludes, "that snow and ice are the most destructive climatic agents to the bobwhite quail on the northern edge of its range. They operate either by cutting off the birds' food supply or by killing them directly when accompanied by strong winds and low temperatures. It is the exceptional year which kills the quail, and it has been estimated that such a winter in the north central region (Wisconsin, Michigan, Iowa, Illinois, Indiana, Ohio) can be expected every 4 to 7 years."

THE SOUTHERN EDGE

Along the Gulf of Mexico lies a narrow strip of the quail range which is tempered with the warm waters of the Gulf. Its winter temperatures are not severe, seldom dropping below the freezing point. Snow visits the southern edge so rarely that a boy may grow to manhood without seeing it in his extremely southern home. This strip of the range runs from the Rio Grande to the Atlantic Ocean, including all of Florida and a belt roughly 50 miles wide across the states between. No definite line, however, can separate the southern edge from the heart of the range lying north of it.

Even this southern edge is not an unlimited paradise for our popular little game bird. Its numbers remain too low to please those who want to hunt. Though we know that foods in the southern part of the range need not be so high in proteins or fats, scientists and hunters alike are beginning to suspect that food is a very important problem anyhow. Green leaves and insects are available nearly the year around, and supply a larger portion of the diet than farther north.

What causes have kept the birds from increasing during the past 50 years in the sunniest section of the South? Heat? Food? Rainfall? Disease? Parasites? Predators? Would there have been any bobwhite quail farther south, had Florida extended toward South America? Or is this southern edge near the climatic extreme in which this kind of bird can reproduce? Part of the questions we can answer. Others are beyond our present knowledge. For now we need only recognize that the southern rim of the United States differs from more northern areas in its treatment of the bobwhite.

THE WESTERN FRINGE

The eastern edge of the Great Plains is the westward edge of the bobwhite range. The line runs through western Nebraska, Kansas, and Oklahoma; and through central Texas, southward into northeast Mexico. Eastward, conditions are favorable for the bobwhite quail. In Texas and Oklahoma the western limits of the bobwhite range merge into the eastern edge of those ranges which are inhabited by the scaled quail and the gambel quail. These two species do not overlap to any appreciable extent with bobwhites. Only a few ranches in a very narrow belt can boast of the presence of bobwhites with any other quail.

The reasons bobwhites live no farther west are only problematical—aridness, wrong foods, or too little of cover. Whatever the true causes, they can be dismissed in practical game conservation with the knowledge that the scaled and gambel quails are well adapted westward and are, therefore, more profitable of care. There are isolated cases of successful transplanting of bobwhites in western states (Washington, Oregon, Idaho, Colorado, New Mexico); but at this time the subject is relatively unimportant to management as we must consider it throughout the vast natural range.

On the east the Atlantic Ocean limits the range of our subject. Thus we have no fringe conditions on the east.

THE HEART OF THE RANGE

The inner and therefore the most significant part of the range has its problems, too, for each and every covey. Life can be and often is made unbearable at any point within it. Millions of acres and many entire farms harbor no quail. Only scattered farms support a high population as we have measured abundance in the past, and many of them have their high carrying capacity only by chance.

Within this inner circle of the bobwhite range man can proceed in quail management—smug in the knowledge that general conditions are favorable. The climate is his ally. The birds have lived hereabouts through countless generations, more or less successful in their struggle for existence. But there the satisfaction of "all-is-well" must stop. Quail management has been retarded by nothing so potent as the general belief that "nature will provide," and that laws would protect. Neither is sufficient.

For 25 years or longer, the hunters and landowners have gone on the assumption: "The quail can take care of themselves in the field." True, the conservation efforts also included excursions into the more artificial means of restoration such as quail hatcheries, restocking, protected refuges, predator control campaigns, educational crusades, and restrictions in bag limits and seasons. But the quail population remained low, became progressively worse. Sadly we must admit: *Quail management is still largely unemployed!*

TABLE 1

AN ESTIMATE OF QUAIL NUMBERS IN THEIR
NATURAL RANGE

State	Number of Farms	Total Acres in States	Estimated * Number of Quail	Number Coveys per Farm	Acres of Land for Each Quail
Ala.	223,369	32,689,920	2,750,000	1	11
Ark.	198,769	33,744,000	3,000,000	1 ¼	11
Conn.	22,241	3,135,360	20,000	—	150
Del.	9,296	1,265,920	15,000	—	80
Fla.	61,159	34,727,680	2,500,000	3	14

TABLE 1 (*continued*)

State	Number of Farms	Total Acres in States	Estimated * Number of Quail	Number Coveys per Farm	Acres of Land for Each Quail
Ga.	225,897	37,451,520	3,000,000	1	12
Ill.	204,239	35,806,080	2,000,000	1⅓	17
Ind.	175,970	23,171,200	2,000,000	1	12
Iowa	208,934	35,830,400	1,400,000	½	25
Kan.	141,192	52,552,320	1,000,000	½	50
Ky.	238,501	25,669,760	1,600,000	½	16
La.	129,295	28,913,280	2,000,000	1¼	14
Mexico (northeastern states)			1,600,000	—	—
Md.	41,275	6,327,680	400,000	¾	16
Mass.	37,007	5,060,480	10,000	—	500
Mich.	175,268	36,494,080	300,000	—	120
Minn.	188,952	51,205,760	100,000	—	500
Miss.	263,528	30,348,800	3,750,000	1	8
Mo.	242,934	44,332,800	5,400,000	1½	8
Nebr.	111,756	49,058,560	1,000,000	1	50
N. J.	26,226	4,814,080	100,000	⅓	48
N. Y.	149,490	30,674,560	20,000	—	—
N. C.	287,412	31,450,880	3,000,000	1	10
Ohio	220,575	26,318,080	1,000,000	⅓	26
Okla.	164,790	44,341,120	3,000,000	½	15
Penna.	171,761	28,828,800	600,000	⅓	48
R. I.	3,603	677,120	10,000	⅓	68
S. C.	147,745	19,580,160	2,000,000	1	10
Tenn.	234,431	26,855,040	1,500,000	½	17
Texas	384,977	168,732,160	12,000,000	3	14
Va.	173,051	25,535,360	3,000,000	1½	8
W. Va.	97,600	15,417,600	400,000	⅓	38
Wisc.	177,745	35,017,600	500,000	—	70
Total	5,138,988	1,026,028,160	60,975,000		
	555,000**	171,000,000**			
					Average
Net Total	4,583,988	855,028,160	60,975,000	1	14

* These estimates are for the fall (1948). Accuracy is not claimed.
** Approximate number of farms (and acreage) beyond the quail range in Mich., Minn., Nebr., N. Y., Texas, and Wisc.

CHAPTER II
PREVAILING PROBLEMS

The bobwhite range encompasses approximately 855 million acres of land in 32 states. Within the same area live 115 million people, which is 82 percent of the population of the United States.

Each citizen of hunting age and inclination may have asked himself at some time, "What is my rightful heritage in bobwhites? How many of the little birds is my fair share? How generously has the state provided me with hunting of the eastern quail?"

Many have never asked themselves those questions. Perhaps game technicians and administrators, too, have never thought about it much. How well have we provided that "right of every man to the pursuit of hunting" which we so glibly defend? Will a realistic look be disappointing?

An inquiry of the 32 states as to their bobwhite populations in 1947 brought many replies of "no information" as to numbers, but they "wish we knew." A few gave estimates from surveys and studies conducted in recent years by their game technicians. From their estimates and my own calculations, I put the total number of bobwhites at 60 million birds in the fall of 1948; or 30 million (one-half) in the spring of 1949. Those estimates by states are given in Table 1. Frankly, we need not be too greatly concerned, for the purpose of the theme in this book, whether these numbers are a little too high or a little too low. Any reasonable figures will help. Let's see what these mean.

Sixty million birds is only half a bird per person; but, of course, everyone doesn't hunt. The number of hunting licenses issued in 1948 by these 32 states was above 8 million. Admittedly, every hunter who buys a license doesn't hunt bobwhites. On the other hand, landowners are privileged to hunt without licenses; and this group numbers one or more persons on each of four and a half million farms.

Sixty million birds is only one bird for every 14 acres of land in the quail range. It averages out to be one covey per farm, since the average farm is 200 acres in size.

Sixty million birds would provide no more than 6 or 7 birds a year for each farm owner to harvest if he allowed none of his friends to hunt. Sixty million birds would allow less than 4 birds annually for each licensed hunter (if the landowner refrained from hunting). The harvest will not exceed half the fall population (or 30 million out of 60). Obviously 60 million is not enough quail for the quail hunters. Thirty million is not enough for the American hunters' bags.

An area of 855 million acres is a vast amount of land which could produce many million more quail than it does: certainly double that number, and probably more. About two-thirds of this land is privately owned farms, ranches and woodland holdings, on which nearly the entire quail population is produced and hunted. The remaining land is in cities, roads and public lands which produce only a minor portion of the quail. Quail abundance has not been achieved by the states and their licensed hunters who once claimed the responsibility. It must be accomplished, if ever, by the four and a half million (4,500,000) landowners upon whose properties the birds spend their lives.

Any way we say it, the bobwhite population is far from enough. On many farms and in numerous localities the birds have become fewer, even to the vanishing point. The landowner who claims to have more birds than ever before is a very rare person, indeed.

The extremist may predict "In another 10 years you won't be able to find a quail outside a museum or a quail hatchery," as we sometimes hear in the conversation of the hopeless. But there is no immediate danger of a catastrophe such as that. We can shrug away those oft-repeated warnings that unless we do something about the situation "quail will go the way of the passenger pigeon." What we are really concerned about is how to produce more birds than we have now on the privately-owned and publicly-managed lands throughout the range.

The present situation nearly screams the thought: "Wildlife conservation as practiced the last 25 years has failed to increase the number of bobwhites." Is that an indictment against our laws? Or against our scientific knowledge? Or sportsmen? Or the stewards of the land? Well—for the moment we need only to admit that quail conservation is not a gratifying success. Let's take a look at the present situation; and dig into the forces which we had hoped would turn the trend upward. For it is true that we have been expecting an increase in one way or another for periods much longer than a reasonable time to await anticipated results. What of our laws, practices, and techniques?

Laws, and regulations having the force of laws, protect quail to a certain extent from hunters. Every state has laws, and, in spite of numerous claims to the contrary, enforce them in a reasonably satisfactory manner. The states which have the best enforcement do not, surprisingly, have noticeably more birds than the "lax" states enjoy. Furthermore, the length of season seems to have little protective effect. Oklahoma, with its 20-day season (3 days a week), has no edge on the six southeastern states of Alabama, Florida, Georgia, Louisiana, Mississippi, and South Carolina, which permit from 70 to 90 days continuous hunting (except Sundays). In general (and specifically): Laws may have kept the downward trend gentle, but no increase of quail has ever been proven a result of laws—even in the case of inviolate sanctuaries where all hunting was eliminated.

Leopold (1940) said it this way: "Wildlife conservation began with the idea of *prohibitions* . . . but after a century of trial it seems apparent that they give more aid and comfort to wildlifers than to wildlife. Prohibitions are a necessary springboard to positive action, but in and of themselves they are negative and accomplish little."

Refuges. Ohio had the doubtful honor of learning that a continuous closed season did not benefit the state-wide population materially. This was a case of a state-wide refuge. It was continued many years without notable increases.

The 100,000 acre state refuge in Ellis County, Oklahoma,

has had no more quail at any time than it did before hunting was stopped in 1921—a 27-year failure to increase the birds by protection.

The Federal Government acquired something more than 2,390,000 acres in 92 projects for its submarginal land purchase program of the 1930's. These are widely scattered purchases in 21 states in the range of the bobwhite quail. For the first 2 or 3 years numbers did increase due to food abundance in idle fields. Three to five years later the retired farm lands had fewer birds than when the Government bought them; in spite of no hunting, considerable restocking, and almost no disturbance of nesting areas and coverts. Refuges, though useful to some species, proved of little value to bobwhites.

Predator control appeared, with some logic, to hold much promise to protect birds in their natural habitats. Current writers still harp on the predator theory. Paul Errington (1946) studied the subject of predation most thoroughly, including most of the literature on the subject. He concluded that predators have little if any significant influence on populations of game. Most technicians agree that predator control was only a false hope and should be recognized as such.

Quail hatcheries had their fling as the conservation hope through the 1920's and 1930's. Artificial restocking still has many disciples. The successful introduction of the ring-necked pheasant was attributed to the game farms. It played an important part in the beginning, but the rapid increase from a few to huntable surpluses of pheasants was largely a result of the highly favorable field conditions in adaptable states.

Quail hatcheries had several faults: They were too expensive; diseases were prevalent; and most important, it was a false belief to expect raised birds to increase where wild birds had failed to do so. Unlike the pheasant, the bobwhite was native and had already reached numbers as large as his environment would allow.

Virginia had the first sizeable quail farm, established in 1920. With few exceptions every state established a quail hatchery. Some bought birds from other states, notably from Mississippi, Texas and Mexico. The highest number of birds released in a single year was below 300,000. As late as 1948, some states still operated quail hatcheries. Many admit the value of pen-raised quail is "only for public relations." We could close this false hope by asking: "What can we expect of a few thousand pen-reared quail where 60 million native birds cannot increase?"

Raising quail in the back yard is a pleasant hobby but not a sound endeavor in conservation. The sacrifice of precious funds to operate quail hatcheries in the name of "public relations" is simply a result of pressure from uninformed hunters. One covey of quail on a farm of average size (200 acres or smaller) makes it unnecessary to stock it with pen-raised birds. Stocking is absolutely indefensible except where no quail exist close by— and then only after adequate food and shelter have grown to maturity. Every sportsman and every landowner should accept this principle.

Education, too, failed to sweep upward bobwhite populations. Education has accompanied every idea in conservation. It seeks to accomplish the task in three ways: (1) raising enthusiasm and desire for more birds; (2) teaching the sportsmen a creed of self-restraint, law abidance, and gentleness; and (3) instructions to apply numerous conservation measures believed adequate to improve the birds' living conditions afield. Unfortunately we haven't known quite the right things to teach, at least not the most essential ones. Furthermore, we should never expect education to accomplish all the functions of encouragement and explanation which are needed to attain actual management. Too much dependence on education alone will allow quail numbers to remain low.

All of these earlier measures were conceived in sincerity, and amid confidence rivalled only by hopes. They were the best methods then known. To say "they failed to increase bobwhites" does not imply total failure. We must have laws and education. Nonetheless we must have the "know-how" to grow bobwhites in spots where none are able to exist today; to increase them where their numbers are meager and coveys are scattered; and to reach greater abundance yet on well stocked lands.

Since laws and refuges, predator control and restocking and education have failed to restore our bobwhites and increase their numbers, what of land management?

THE PROBLEMS OF LAND MANAGEMENT

The first concerted efforts to learn the secrets of quail management were revealed in 1931 with the publication of "The Bobwhite Quail, Its Habits, Preservation, and Increase" by Herbert L. Stoddard (Charles Scribner's Sons, New York). Actually the quest had just begun in earnest. Publication of the book was only a milestone—not the end of the road.

Stoddard's book gave full expression to what was then known on the subject of the bobwhite quail. Most of its excellent contents were learned by Stoddard and his associates during their intensive study of the bird in the southeastern states in the five-year period of 1924–29. From that state of game management a great interest and a great hope arose throughout the nation for "insuring in perpetuity an abundance of bobwhites and the enjoyment of the sport of quail hunting" (from the foreword). The last paragraph of its introduction contains the modest statement, "The scientific workers of the investigation are fully aware . . . that many of the problems attacked are little more than opened up for further study." It is a significant fact that much progress has been made since the late '20's.

In 1933 appeared the formal presentation of "Game Management" by Aldo Leopold (Charles Scribner's Sons, New York). Both Leopold's and Stoddard's books were "attempts to describe the art of cropping land for game and to point the way toward its integration with other ends in land-use." These works inspired the budding profession of wildlife management. Game managers, teachers, biologists, foresters, agriculturists, and sportsmen found the principles and practices set forth logical, promising, and guiding.

From out of these two works more than anything else came principles of game management, taught in every school of wildlife management, and quoted by most contemporary authors. Thus have come many of our common beliefs among sportsmen, scientists, and laymen as regard quail and the problems of their management. Unfortunately, a number of common beliefs still persist in error, even though Stoddard and Leopold exposed them as such many years ago.

Since the late '20's, which cast their influence on these writings, considerable work has been done by numerous students of the subject. In 1932 the American Game Association, with the aid of the Bureau of Biological Survey and a few state game departments, set out to demonstrate game management according to the Stoddard and Leopold techniques. Eleven areas deemed suitable were selected in the states of South Carolina, Louisiana, Arkansas, Alabama, Indiana, Oklahoma, and Wisconsin. I managed the most western one: in Ellis County, Oklahoma.

Nine of the projects "folded up" before three years had expired. My own work carried through three years and a half. Quite bluntly: We failed to demonstrate successful land management for quail! Much of my work turned to experimental studies in search of more successful techniques; and to study of the birds' habits in western areas as compared to the southeast. Thus I was privileged to be one of the first to learn the heartbreaking truth—that game management techniques were not as good as we had hoped so sincerely.

Since 1932 we have never despaired of ultimate success. Neither have we dodged the challenge to develop new methods that might produce the results we sought. Others have worked similarly on the problems. We may now add the experience of 20-odd years of trial (and often tribulation) to the earlier concepts. Refinements, new discoveries, and even what may seem to be contradictions are nothing more than normally progressive developments.

Though the hopes of 20 years ago have not borne fruit abundantly, the ideas still grow. To date they have produced three things: (1) a little success, (2) alarming disappointments, and (3) new hopes again. It is unprofitable to try to decide at this point why bobwhite management failed to produce the results we all hoped for. Better, it seems, to discuss more of the factors which may shed light on our present needs.

The history of our country's development is from a wilderness—with less than a million Indians and no cattle, horses, or other domestic livestock—to an agricultural and industrial nation of 150 million persons. This vast increase in people and livestock altered the cover and food for birds and thus influenced their numbers. Nevertheless we can limit our discussion to the conditions we are now facing, looking backward no more than a few years to pick up essential knowledge bearing on management. (In the case of quail, historical study has shed no important light on modern management, either by studies of conditions in Indian times, the days of the pioneers, or the rapid development of agriculture.)

We can begin, then, about 20 years ago when Stoddard and Leopold pointed the way to wildlife management. One of their principal objectives was: adequate food and cover through the medium of land management. They knew and wrote that laws and incidental management of land were not enough. Since then, unfortunately, the food and cover phase of conservation was never given sufficient attention by hunters, nor by the agencies to whom hunters looked for game conservation. Land management has been the stepchild of wildlife restoration. It has not been taken universally into the family circle.

Leopold, in his preface to the Game Survey of the North Central States (1931), wrote: "Our legislatures decree game conservation; our sportsmen and nature-lovers resolve we shall have it, but our landowners do not practice it, nor are they offered any inducement or motive, other than altruism, for doing so. . . . Such is our impasse. Some more tenable relationship between landowners, the game, and the public is obviously needed. The farm seemed the place to seek light on what it should be." Thus we began to see land management as an essential in production of bobwhites.

We may enjoy his deep foresight further by quoting more of his thinking in those pioneer days of land management for game. He tells of a 280-acre farm in Calloway County, Missouri, which had 210 bobwhites in 1923 but only 90 in 1930. He named the cause when he surmised the reduction came with and because of more land brought to pasturage and the destruction of brush coverts, particularly along field boundaries. Then he showed a map including improvements he would suggest be made; but fearfully he wrote, "Whether agricultural experts would approve this particular reconstruction is not known. Probably not." His major plea was "that they start experiments on this question, and tell farmers what particular measures for the benefits of game *would* meet with their approval, and what response in game might be expected."

The number of farms with similar experiences is doubtless in the hundreds of thousands, but most of the agricultural agencies did not heed Leopold's plea. It remained for a national agency concerned with land management in all its phases to demonstrate land management practices for the bobwhite quail. The Soil Conservation Service perceived those opportunities. Its leaders recognized their own responsibilities in this direction, and began in the mid-1930's to adapt soil and water conservation practices to land use, including those of value to wildlife on privately owned land.

The importance of soil conservation and land use is best understood by a joint survey conducted about that time by the Fish and Wildlife Service (then the Bureau of Biological Survey) and the Bureau of Agricultural Economics (Miller and Powell

in 1942). Their report stated: "The findings are of such importance to both the conservation of wildlife and to agriculture that
they should be kept constantly in mind when formulating programs or studies dealing with wildlife and its utilization.

"The study disclosed the fact that 87 percent of the land
considered potentially available for wild-game production and
use is devoted primarily to agricultural purposes, and when it is
realized that almost 100 percent of the agricultural land has
some wildlife potentialities, the value of this study to both the
farmers and the conservationists is understandable." That survey, coupled with some newly forming ideas of farm practices,
focused national attention on agriculture as an essential factor
in game restoration.

From that year on an increasing number of people began
to think that wildlife conservation is more of an agricultural
problem than scientists, game wardens, sportsmen, and landowners had ever admitted before. Certainly, farming had much
to do with the cover and food of bobwhites and other farm-
game. According to Dr. Rudolph Bennitt (1937), Missouri game
scientist and professor, "The techniques of developing and maintaining food and cover . . . constitute about nine-tenths of all
game management."

At the same time Leopold (1937) said, "Our conservation
department faces a public which still thinks a few eggs will solve
the game problem. . . . That public is not even conscious of
the basic fact that the history of resources is written not by government, but by the farmers who own land and the consumers
who buy its products."

The truth is, however, that what to do and how to get it
done was largely untried theory. We had no patterns of success-

ful farm management to follow. Confirming this fact Leopold in 1938 made the astonishing statement: "Fifteen years ago we started out to discover, by research, how wildlife can be increased by means of management. Have we succeeded? My answer is 'No'. . . . That is to say, the hoped-for discoveries, leading promptly and directly to successful management, have not, in most cases, been forthcoming. . . . Can we tell the Wisconsin landowners today 'apply our techniques and you will have a reasonably dependable quail crop?' No, we cannot."

To recognize that bobwhite management is wrapped up in some sort of a deal with farming is one thing. To realize that farming in the whole quail range is pursued as approximately four-and-a-half million separate enterprises (privately owned) is quite another. The boldest conservationist might be pardoned if he shrank from the perplexing and apparently hopeless task of leading such an unwieldy mass of human endeavor. There have been, of course, the educational avenues of sportsmen's clubs, 4-H clubs, high schools, colleges, books, bulletins, magazines, news items and lectures. But these are not enough. They have been employed in such an endeavor for scores of years.

In the beginning the Soil Conservation Service, though believing in these educational methods also, had plans for demonstrating land management more far reaching than any other organization could have foreseen at that time.

The new movement which was under way was not clearly evident for a decade or more. The new opportunities to study and apply game production were a part of a new organization of farmers themselves: THE SOIL CONSERVATION DISTRICT. Theirs is a legal subdivision of state government organized and run by farmers who became determined to conserve their soil and water

resources by every sound measure of land-use and land management. By 1935 the Secretary of Agriculture had determined that
erosion control, water conservation, and dependable land use
must be furthered through these organized efforts of farmers.

The Soil Conservation Service was charged by Congress
with the national responsibility to give land-use guidance and
assistance to American farmers. Its chief, Dr. H. H. Bennett,
had recognized game conservation as one of the several benefits
to be expected from sound land management. He believed game
management measures could be used to prevent erosion and to
conserve water and moisture. Game would make profitable use
of certain kinds of land. Consequently, the new agricultural
Service focused its major attention on soil conservation districts,
and sought to help them attain worth-while objectives in land
management.

When it came to the welfare of bobwhites, the Service
found the way poorly marked except in theory. The recommendations of the 1930's lacked experience, successful application,
and simplicity. A number of the ideas advocated were not sound.
No one knew how farmers would receive the suggestions; therefore, we began to learn by trial how to approach their problems
with them.

Game writers advocated the retirement of eroded lands—
gullies, small fields, and corners—for wildlife coverts and feeding
areas. "Plant them with shrubs and vines and grasses. Stop
erosion. Give the birds cover and food," went the advice. But
what to plant was a pertinent question. It would be unfair to
say that wildlife management experts didn't know what to plant.
They knew almost every shrub and vine and grass in the world,
and they advocated every one that might be of any use whatso-

ever. The problem soon became one of knowing which plants to discard so nurseries would know what to raise, technicians would know what to recommend, and landowners could afford to use them. We soon learned that gullies can be controlled best with kudzu in certain sections; that gullies in woodland will soon turn to woods regardless of the wildlife shrubs we bravely started with. We learned, too, that gullies protected from grazing in prairie sections became good cover of a sort, good nesting areas for example. The trend in gully control was to simplification.

Some ardent wildlife conservationists accepted the knowledge that bobwhites find many kinds of food on idle fields. Disking retards broomsedge and trees, favoring lespedezas, beggarweeds, ragweeds, sunflowers, and partridge peas—temporarily. Many made the mistake of advocating idle-field management to farmers who couldn't afford idle fields. Idle land, it should be known, only occurs on a farm because it has become unprofitable for the crops the farmer formerly grew. It is a symbol of waste, misuse, and often abuse. No agricultural agency could accept a program of game conservation based on misused land because it wasn't sound. The farmers wouldn't knowingly plan such operations. Of course, the districts refused to countenance idle land. They had declared their intention of outlawing all idle land. Farmers needed its production of grass, or hay, or timber to make their own food and shelter better. Disking of idle land went out the soil conservation (and agricultural) window.

Game leaders also recommended fire as a land management tool to keep southeastern woodland in good condition for bobwhites (Stoddard 1931). They also observed that the weed seeds in poorly cultivated cropland attracted the birds and fed them through the winter months. These were the most dependable practices then known to keep bobwhites on farms, ranches, and woodland tracts.

The fire recommended was less intense and less destructive than the common type of fire which burned millions of acres of southern woods every spring. Yet, the way managers of most hunting preserves followed the idea was anything but comforting to anyone interested in profitable land use, whether they were foresters, game technicians, or landowners. A full stand of timber obviously wasn't going to grow against the still-too-hot-and-too-frequent fires. To burn or not to burn was a hot question —a serious one.

Weedy cropland had objectionable features, too; far beyond the "pride of clean cultivation" slightingly referred to by numerous writers who sought to instill conservation ideals into farmers. People can starve to death on poor farming. They can ill afford to divide the moisture and fertility of the fields in grain ripening time with weeds which only support a covey or two of birds. Anyone could see readily that the type of poor farming which supported quail best fed people worst.

Though annual burning, weedy farming, and plenty of idle land actually supported more quail than any other practices, these were ideas few landowners could afford to follow. People in agriculture deplored what they considered ill advised suggestions from those who obviously knew little of farm economy.

Through these early years of the soil conservation era, a few of the men who had long been guiding conservation thinking saw that wildlife management was not getting results, was not being practiced. The gist of their symposium (Bode, Gordon, 1938) "How Best to Plan for Wildlife in Land Management" (Third North American Wildlife Conference, Baltimore, Md.)

was fourfold: (1) measures must be few and simple; (2) if we cannot show how wildlife management can fit into regularly accepted forms of land use and land practice, we are not going to get very far; (3) uncertainty whether we knew what to do; and (4) agreement that we had not been able to set up the machinery to apply management practice, or to get help to the people who live upon the land.

Thus by 1940 a reversal of traditional relationship was evolving between sportsmen and farmers. We once believed bobwhite restoration to be a sportsman's problem in which farmers might be persuaded to cooperate. Actually it is an agricultural problem to which hunters must find some way to contribute. It was only natural, then, that the Soil Conservation Service inherited the national leadership in restoration of bobwhites and other wildlife species insofar as private land management contributes to the objective.

Thus from a look at the past and present we summarize by concluding:

1. Laws, predator control, hatcheries, refuges, and education have not been sufficient to meet the needs of bobwhite quail anywhere in their extensive range.

2. No state claims to have more birds afield today. "Conservation" has not "saved" quail hunting. Management has not been successful. We must now "produce" if we are to reclaim good hunting.

3. The techniques of management, having failed, warrant searching investigation for faults and failures.

4. Land management for bobwhites must become recognized as an agricultural problem, revolutionary as the idea may seem.

CHAPTER III
TRADITIONS TO FORGET

The foregoing chapter explores fallacies of some of our cherished traditions. Incidentally, "traditions" are only "the oral handing down of information, opinions, and doctrines, through successive generations, as from father to son." They are often guilty of delaying enlightened knowledge, because traditions may be "any belief that owes its general acceptance to habit rather than to reason."

Traditions in game management, specifically bobwhite management, exist as a formidable power; particularly when the traditions are as "cherished" as our common beliefs which surround this friendly farm bird. This chapter exposes a number of false traditions. The situation during the past 25 years has been serious enough to warrant a few shocks and some disillusionment. Actually, many widely heralded techniques of management have been found impractical, and generally unsuccessful. To have more bobwhites, we must have several changes in our most cherished traditions!

Land management appeared years ago to be the way forward. It still is! In spite of this truth, our bird population has not increased in any significant amount anywhere. This has been true on individual farms, in every state as a whole, and across the entire range of the bobwhite quail. Obviously, something has been wrong!

A number of things were wrong. Added together we may say the recommendations were too complex. They included many nonessential items which wasted much effort, and produced no results. Both scientists and laymen also believed that quail need many things they do not. Landowners falsely assumed that their land had plenty of the essentials when actually the life-sustaining requirements were absent or scant. Many would have done the right things sooner, if they had known what to do.

Bobwhite management is not very complicated. In fact it is less complex than we realized. It is more simple than laymen believed. Moreover, the essential things in bobwhite management do not include many of the traditions formerly accepted. The following examples are interesting.

WATER TO DRINK

Bobwhites do not need water to drink. They get moisture from their foods. Neither dew nor surface water is essential. The proof and explanation of this almost unbelievable fact is discussed in more detail in the chapter "The Bobwhites' Habits". With the old belief out of the way, people can raise their eyes to the dry upland areas and see quail management in a new and better light.

GRIT FOR DIGESTION

Occasionally, people have used a lack of grit as an alibi for poor results with winter feeding in the snow country. It sounded quite logical that grit was necessary to help grind the hard seeds in the gizzard. Surprisingly, grit is not necessary at all (Nestler 1946).

Extensive studies of pen-reared quail disclosed that birds are able to digest foods such as corn, millet, milo, soybeans, field peas, vetch, and lespedezas without any grit. The investigators raised chicks from the egg to maturity with no grit. They also carried adult birds through an entire winter without loss of weight or health. Furthermore, the birds went through the entire breeding season without grit or gravel.

Though the birds do not require it, they generally have some grit in the gizzard. Once having it, experiments disclosed, they could retain grit for a period of five months after being deprived of a fresh supply. Even if you believe grit a necessity, you need no longer fear that birds will perish for lack of it during the northern blizzards. The South has not been concerned seriously with grit as a false problem.

DISEASE

No management has been found necessary yet against a single disease of bobwhites in the field. The birds are wonderfully healthy as long as they are well fed. Forget about disease. It is a problem of the quail hatchery, not of field management.

POISONOUS SEEDS

Unfortunately, several plants produce abundant seeds that quail will not eat. "If quail would only eat coffee weed seeds, we'd feed 'em without fail" is a common lament in the south. Many people fear "poisonous" seeds are responsible for low quail population. Fear not! Quail have more sense than to eat them. As Nestler and Bailey (1941) explained in reference to crotalaria, bobwhites refuse to eat the seed; "some individuals starve rather than eat the toxic material;" and "if a few seeds are picked up accidentally . . . they will be evacuated from the bowels undigested."

Quail evidently choose their foods quite wisely. Of course, they must have good ones available, as discussed in the chapter on foods.

NATURE WILL PROVIDE

No fallacy is greater than the smugly incorrect assumption that nature will provide for wild creatures. We cannot depend on nature to provide abundance of bobwhites. Protection of native vegetation is not enough. Mother Nature seldom selects her plants to feed and shelter bobwhites; her choice of plants is more often grasses, trees, and shrubs which provide more than enough cover, but little or no food for quail in winter. Man can grow and feed bobwhites better than nature.

If you live in the heart of the bobwhite range, look for the food plants in your woods and on the stream banks and hedges and field borders. These areas grow with a preponderance of plants entirely useless to bobwhite quail. If you live in the northern fringe, compare the natural shelter of leafless hardwoods with the protective values of evergreens which you could select and plant. The habitat of the semi-arid western fringe needs added cover and better foods to replace the superabundance of the nesting and roosting covers of the native grasses. In peninsular Florida and the rim of the Gulf, nature provides too much cover—mats of grasses, palmettos, and tree leaves too heavy for the use of quail. No, you cannot have bobwhites in abundance if you try to let nature do it.

Man and management are intelligent. By them nature can be bent into better patterns for man's purposes. Management is the selection of suitable foods and cover, and their establishment and care in a sound land-use economy.

RELUCTANCE TO EAT A NEW FOOD

If you should try the new plant—bicolor lespedeza (a perennial, woody legume which produces a seed of particular value to bobwhites)—don't worry about the false idea, prevalent in most game circles, that quail will take two or three years to "get used to a new food." They'll eat bicolor or any good food the first time they see it.

That idea of quail being cautious in accepting new foods disturbs a lot of people. I know a man who is still hoping his birds will eat crotalaria, though they have refused to do so for 15 years. You should not let "quail reluctance to eat new foods" become one of *your* "cherished traditions."

Quail will eat a *good* food when they find it in sufficiency. They will resist a poor one until starved to eating it.

BIRDS CONTROL INSECTS AND WEEDS

To say "bobwhites and other birds destroy insects and weed

seeds" is correct. The birds eat large numbers of both. To say "bobwhites and other birds *control* insects and weeds for the farmer", however, is verging on the very gullible. Every acre has hundreds of thousands of insects. The birds eat many; but far from all of them. Plenty will be left to increase to destructive proportions next year if conditions are favorable enough. But insects, too, have their hazards against multiplication without restraint. Actually the greatest enemies of insects are bad weather and other kinds of insects. Maybe the bobwhites help a little bit.

The farmer can be told "there ain't no Santa Claus" without ruining his Christmas Day. A man trying to manage for bobwhites needs to know the true relationship between his birds and their foods. The essential fact is that insects, better than any other foods, support quail in summer. Weed seeds are important supplements in summer; and, also, to any essential winter food which may be grown for the bobwhites. So we can depend on insects and weed seeds for summer foods—this is the fact that should become traditional.

VARIETY, AS A PRINCIPLE IN QUAIL FOODS

This concept has so confused the thinking of scientists and laymen that bobwhites have been poorly fed when great effort was expended in their behalf. Variety is not essential. Quail do not choose it of their own free will. To feed birds well requires abundance of a good food at every season of the year. This may be one kind of seed grown for the entire winter's food supply. It will be largely insects for the summer. Practical management needs to be simple of application. The simpler way has proven successful. See more detail in the chapter on foods.

POOR LAND MEANS FEW QUAIL

A number of surveys have shown that large areas of thin, infertile soil support fewer coveys than the more fertile areas in similar use (Stoddard, 1931, and Bennitt, 1937). From their conclusions you may surmise that quail management is useless or hopeless in such areas. Far from it. The poorer areas promise to become the real strongholds for increased populations. Poor lands offer permanent opportunities for sound management of bobwhites, particularly in and around the woodland of every farm and timber holding. Possibly on range land, too.

ROOM FOR WILDLIFE LAND 662675

It is common talk that farmers cannot afford to set aside land for the sole purpose of growing birds. This is far from true. A survey made in 1946 by the Soil Conservation Service in nine southeastern states shows 8 million acres of idle land in a 155 million total. This is equal to 5 percent of the land. Wildlife land for quail production requires only 1 or 2 percent of woodland areas, and 3 to 5 percent of cropland fields.

Wildlife borders, for example, are placed on what is now called cropland, though the sapped edge fails to produce profitable field crops. The conversion of this cropland to wildlife land is economically sound. It is an intelligent recognition of former misuse which reduced farming profits; a realization that wildlife land is less wasteful.

Similarly, bicolor lespedeza strips can be placed in the numerous unproductive openings which occur in southern pine woods. That reduces timber production none at all. Of course a landowner can afford wildlife land. He has only waited for a practice which actually produces birds for his efforts.

FOOD GROWS ABUNDANTLY

If you had read all the reports from scientific studies on the problems of quail management, you would be shocked at the frequent statement "good quail foods are abundant." The authors then hasten on to find some other factor which might be responsible for the low population. Actually, foods throughout the range of the bobwhites are scarce and tedious for the birds to find. The exception is with certain kinds of cultivation. Before you argue that feed is no problem, consider: (1) its abundance from October to May, particularly January through March; (2) the competition of sparrows, doves, rabbits, pheasants, deer, rats, field mice, and—above all—livestock; (3) how thinly the seeds are upon the ground and (4) whether there is a crop of food *every* year near each good area of cover. If not, food is not abundant; it is uncertain, scarce, and misleading. The most advancement in quail management has come recently with the provision of food.

WINTER FEEDING

Winter feeding in the northern states is an expensive and none too successful method of quail management. The "emergency" type of feeding deserves severe condemnation.

As Gerstel (1942) so well stated, "The basis . . . of large scale winter feeding programs is composed of two principal components, namely: (a) an instinctive urge, common to a large percentage of all humans, to provide animals observed during severe weather with food; and (b) a general, though inexplicable and indefensible, belief that shootable game crops can annually be produced only through the provision of supplemental winter food supplies."

Many northern scientists have become convinced that artificial feeding is hopeless. They recognize that competition among bobwhites and rabbits, field rats, pheasants, and many lesser birds is a very serious barrier to success. (Hawkins 1937, Fry 1938, Allen 1938).

THE FEAR OF INBREEDING OR SOMETHING

An idea is prevalent that a covey will be benefited by shooting some of the birds, "to scatter them." It must have come from two theories: (1) since an unshot covey never gets any bigger nor multiplies to two or more where only one grew the year before, something might be wrong with their breeding abilities; (2) it's an argument an eager hunter likes to give the landowner who would rather have no hunting.

The first problem deserves a correct answer. There is nothing wrong with the breeding ability of the unshot covey. Coveys larger than 15 to 18 birds are remarkable. Large coveys are quite exceptional and not to be expected in any case. Bobwhite habit is to remain in coveys of 12 to 15 birds, or less. We do not see the multiplication because we have done nothing to support a second covey nearby—the surplus moves elsewhere or dies attempting to find a suitable home.

Everyone knows that shooting a few birds does not scatter the covey except for a few hours. Also, dead birds won't breed as well as live ones.

SECOND COVEYS AND LATE HATCHES

A few people still believe quail may raise two broods of young in one year—an early hatch cared for by the cock and a late one raised by both parents. Stoddard called this a false idea twenty years ago for Georgia and Florida. Errington echoed the proof in Iowa in 1932. We found it untrue beyond doubt for Oklahoma in 1932, '33, '34, and '35.

I have flushed birds three or four weeks old, with young of twice their size or more, on several occasions. On my own study area, I knew the summer coveys and their location to an exactness. It is the one place we have known where we could find the same birds every day. Once located, we could show any visitor the coveys he wished to indicate on our map—show them without fail on the following day. Such an opportunity permitted observations with marvelous accuracy. What appeared to be two ages of young in one covey were: one covey moved by our activities into a second, whence both flushed together. The next day they would be separate again; in fact, they were separate though near each other only a few minutes before being disturbed.

The hen and cock birds are obviously satisfied with their efforts for the entire season if they have even a single chick to rear, which happens occasionally. Their instincts of parenthood are not satisfied with anything less than a chick, however. They will nest and renest all summer if their efforts are completely destroyed each time.

I recorded a nest hatch in Oklahoma sandhills November 2, 1933, two days after the first fall frost. We had other nests come off in September (and possibly October) but wild quail hatching after mid-September have no chance to live through the chilly nights of late October and November. The few "squealers" (half grown birds) at Thanksgiving time were 9 or 10 weeks old. The total of these late hatches is negligible. Shed no tears and hold no fears. Such occurrences have no significance to our hunting populations.

REFUGES AND TRANSPLANTING

Trapping quail on refuges to transplant elsewhere is of no consequence. The total number has no significance where related to a state's population of birds. Food and cover conditions can be improved at less cost than the transplanting. Birds will move into good homes.

Management of refuges has not been efficient enough to produce any but negligible surpluses of birds. Leopold in 1931 was searching for every possible means of quail management. He discarded such foolish ideas as shooting-up the fall coveys to prevent inbreeding; but he labelled as "entirely practicable" the transplanting of birds from "quail refuges." His hopes have not materialized; time and experience proved refuges largely ineffective. This tradition may be difficult for a few oldtimers to give up but not one hunter or farmer in a hundred practices this idea any more. Unfortunately several state game departments still expend some of their precious funds on quail refuges and transplanting. The same states often claim they do not have enough money to adequately study or demonstrate the more promising techniques of land management.

THE BIRDS BELONG TO THE STATE. EVERYONE HAS A RIGHT TO HUNT.

According to the laws, the birds belong to the states, and the states offer every one of their citizens the right to hunt bobwhites during open seasons, provided they buy licenses. Unfortunately, this appearance of privilege to share commonly in nature's bounties measures up ridiculously short of any reasonable expectation in the case of bobwhites. As pointed out elsewhere, for every bobwhite there are two persons living within the quail range. The states license 6 or 7 million hunters every year. If we divide the killable half of the quail population evenly among the hunters, each would have the grand privilege of killing four or five birds.

You are kidding yourself and your fellow sportsmen if you resist the idea of posted farms, leased hunting rights, and hunting limited to the landowners and their friends or business associates. You might as well abandon, now, the useless theory of free hunting, the false hope of abundance for everyone.

Neither the law nor the state can husband the birds upon the land. If we continue to depend upon the state to manage quail, we'll have fewer and fewer of them as we have already seen. The state can't do it!

Anyone who covets the privilege of good quail hunting will find it increasingly desirable to have friendly relations with someone who owns land. If he wants really good hunting, he will offer material assistance to encourage the landowner to produce more birds than nature has done in past years.

Let the state own the birds! But make it good business for landowners to care for them; and give them support in their determination to say who shall hunt upon their lands, if anyone. This implies a friendly exchange of favors; or a payment for hunting privileges; or, best of all, ownership and management of land for yourself.

Hunting quail is not a fundamental right of every sportsman. It is a privilege—a privilege to be earned by paying the cost of production one way or another.

IN SUMMARY

In summary, the traditional thought that the state and its laws, or that nature will provide for more quail, was erroneous, as we know now after decades of hope followed by failure. It is time to manage bits of land for bobwhites, on each separate farm or ranch or timber holding where birds are wanted. To do so requires: (1) the simplest techniques, (2) attention to the essentials, relieving our minds of unnecessary frills, and (3) the arrangement of wildlife lands as a part of the complete pattern of each man's land management. These new ideas will become traditional too with successful experience.

CHAPTER IV
THE BOBWHITES' HABITS

Each kind of animal requires, or chooses, habits of life somewhat different from all other species, even those living in the same locality. Bobwhites, too, have their own peculiar way of living. We call their unique ways of going through life "their habits." And like humans you will find their habits stubborn against any change except an easier, more delightful way of life. In recognition of this fact a knowledge of their habits is very important to everyone who wants to manage well for them.

Bobwhites require food, shelter, nesting sites, and places to dust themselves. They do not require surface water or dew. An environment embracing (1) suitable foods at all seasons of the year and (2) sufficient cover for protection against storms, heat of the sun, man and other animals, is in general a livable home in which they may pursue life according to their habits.

Life is an endless chain, we hope, for every family of bob-whites. Generation follows generation quickly, only two or three years of life for each. Where shall we break into the family circle to begin to follow them through a year of their troubles and successes?

Spring is as good as any time because the coveys have broken up. New families are in the making. By the time the rows of corn are showing across the fields, the winter coveys are no more. Every female has a mate and, it appears, the pair of birds is quite content to abandon all their cronies of the winter past. A few unmated cocks are whistling "bob-white," "bob-white" from their solitary lonesomeness. A small surplus of cock birds is ever present anywhere you may live in the bobwhite range. A spinster hen is an unheard of possibility.

From the time of pairing off in spring until the fall, the prospective parents devote their efforts to bring off a successful hatch from the eggs in their nest; to feeding themselves and their brood; and to protecting themselves and family against too much sun in the middle of the day and against their enemies both day and night.

Though the hen lays the eggs and in most cases incubates them alone, it is not uncommon for the cock to do the 23-day setting. To lay the eggs and hatch the chicks requires about 40 days. By then it is summer.

Many quail nests are broken up by floods and farming activities. The nests are on the ground. Snakes and skunks and numerous other wildlife eat the eggs when they can find them. Cats and dogs, and foxes and coyotes, occasionally catch the hen upon the nest, destroying eggs and parent at the same time. These are natural hazards that confront every pair, every year. We are not likely to eliminate these destructive causes of nesting loss, though we can reduce them by land management—leaving nesting cover where neither machinery nor grazing will interfere. Control of predators has not resulted in substantially increased production, is therefore only a minor factor.

A nest destroyed only of its eggs is but a temporary catastrophe, aggravating though it may appear to birds and man alike. The hen will rest a week or two, and then begin to lay again in a new nest. Instead of being a regrettable loss, the first nest's destruction is as often a blessing in disguise in Florida and the Gulf Coast region where May and June drouths are prevalent. Dry eggs hatch poorly. High humidity is more conducive to big hatches. Be it bad or good, the parents take advantage of the situation by trying again a second, a third, and even perhaps the fourth time if the hen survives the nest destruction. The fourth try, after most of the summer is spent, will not be successful, of course.

In western Oklahoma a few nests are known to hatch in late September and October. In a practical sense the birds that hatch after September in the South, mid-September in the central range, and after August in the more northern states cannot be counted in the increase. The little birds cannot withstand the chill of early-fall nights unless they are old enough to be feathered well—an age of 6 or 7 weeks at least.

The bobwhite quail is a most persistent parent. Either one of the pair will care for the little brood alone, should its mate be killed. More surprising is the known fact that a bachelor cock will just as diligently care for a foster brood if he can find one

(Stoddard, 1931). Throughout the summer rearing of the young, many pairs are confronted with the unwelcome presence of an unmated cock or two. When seen together in close observation, the unmated cock bird is noted by his shabby-feathered appearance, resulting from repeated attacks by the parent male. The old bachelor suffers these indignities and pain every day, just to be with the coveted family. Bobwhites are devoted to their young ones.

The foods of spring and summer are essentially insects, greens, and summer ripening seeds and fruits. They take what they can get. Insects, better than any other foods, support quail and their growing chicks from early spring until fall. The dependence of our quail population on insects for food is not inconsiderable. A lack of suitable insects for food would have to be made up in some way not known to our profession at the present.

Throughout the spring and summer days the nesting birds and their offspring have the daily need of baths. Not water baths as many of our birds enjoy: Dust-baths to keep the mites and lice in check. Bobwhites live with these annoyances, you see. Much of the day is spent in dusting, between the mid-morning close of the early feeding period and before the late afternoon feeding begins. This is their loafing period; time to dust themselves and complete their toilet by preening their feathers. They also sleep in their daytime retreat.

But all through the summer heat they can live without drinking. Water is not one of the problems of quail management. Many people have wasted kindly efforts building watering troughs for bobwhites, hauling water to keep them filled, and have even drilled wells to furnish the birds this unnecessary element for their welfare.

It is hard for people to believe that quail find dust much more essential than water. Stoddard (1931) told us that quail need no surface water in the Southeast, but his book started the rumor that dew would satisfy the needs of moisture when surface water was lacking. Actually quail require no water at all, not even dew. I learned that under the driest conditions under which bobwhite ever lived.

Our ranch in western Oklahoma during the history-making summer droughts of 1933, 1934, and 1935 went weeks with no drop of water, dew or rain. Temperatures went above 100 degrees day after day, reaching 110, 111 and 112 in several mid-afternoons. In 1934, the longest period of no dew or rain whatsover was 62 days in June, July, and August. Little quail far from water survived in excellent health.

Within the 10,000 acre area of my most careful studies, the only surface water was at 4 stock-water tanks. The tanks ran over on windy days. Quail within walking distance did not come to the open water. They could not have gone without leaving tracks. Even the grasshoppers left the plainest of tracks in the powdery sand about the ponds. Most of the coveys were a quarter-of-a-mile away. Some were a mile from the water-tanks.

Now let me hasten to assure you that bobwhites will drink water. At the same time as above, the windmill at our home pumped water which overflowed into some high weeds, a place of good cover for the day. When the windmill failed to turn, as it often failed for two or three days in July and August, the water seeped away into the sand. The covey of parents and half-grown birds would come into our yard, and line up around the lily pond to drink. They evidently were accustomed to water every day. One evening I returned home to find them sitting in a perfect line on the very edge of our front porch, which was shady. But you mustn't believe from this that front porches are a requirement for a loafing place for bobwhites.

A belief that water is essential is understandable. Many farms actually support quail only along the living streams and springs. The appearance is of water and quail inseparable. The reason is obvious in most cases—only in the added moisture of the creek area is food in sufficient abundance. The amount of food growing on good, moist land is greater than nature provides on drier and less productive soils. Management, however, can provide foods elsewhere.

To us humans, water seems as if it would be as important as food and shelter for bobwhites; as it is to our livestock and poultry. But bobwhites are different. Moisture they need, of course. They get it from insects, from green leaves, and from seeds and fruits.

Berries and fruit are often believed necessary as a source of moisture, in the absence of surface water. Stoddard (1931) wrote of the "Blackbelt" of Alabama and Mississippi: "The fruit supply, so essential to quail, is abundant and well distributed." Actually, fruit does not deserve the label "essential." Thousands of quail are reared from Florida to Michigan, from Virginia to Oklahoma with neither fruits nor water available in summer, and only negligible amounts at any time.

By fall a significant change becomes apparent in the size of the bobwhite families. They no longer live in separate pairs. Every pair has not raised a family of young. Many have failed. But everyone will join some more fortunate group for the winter. Thus the population is grouped in coveys averaging 12 or 13 birds per covey—some young, some old in each.

Most of the young broods have reached the full-grown age of 13 to 14 weeks by October or November. Only an occasional covey is seen of half-grown birds, often called "peepers." Their numbers are negligible.

Fall is the season of plenty—in many places. Food is then more abundant than at any other time of year, more plentiful than the birds can use. Cultivated crops have matured. Sunflowers, ragweed, lespedezas, beggar-weeds, acorns and pine seeds seem to be everywhere. The whole summer's production, in a broad sense, is ready for harvest and storage. Yet there are notable exceptions; in pastures, and (as an extreme example) fields of winter wheat. These exceptions apply to parts of almost every farm within the range. Livestock have prevented seed production of the grasses; plowing has destroyed the waste grain and weed seed in preparation for the fall seeding. Haylands, too, are nearly useless, the foods went into the haystack or barnloft. So there's a falseness in the seeming security of fall abundance.

Fall also sees the first rapid steps in food destruction casting their gathering shadows ahead. In the dairy country of Minnesota and Wisconsin, corn is cut for the silo or hauled to the barn, leaving no waste grain or overhead cover in the field. Livestock are turned into the crop fields to glean a few weeks' "pickings" of stalks and weeds and grass. Blackbirds, sparrows, rabbits, deer, and rats and mice consume great quantities of the foods you want for bobwhites. Their foods are drastically reduced day by day. Ragweed, sunflower, and grain are consumed. Seeds on the ground are trampled into the soil. The grasses that might have given comfort through the cold nights are eaten away or trampled down. Insects crawl into the ground or disappear because they cannot grow again until spring. Abundance changes to scarcity so quickly! Management must come to the rescue; for the habit of eating must be continued.

Where will the covey spend the winter? In the same thicket, around the same field where they lived the winter before? Sometimes they do. Often they don't. They settle down for the winter wherever they find plenty of food in or near good cover. Here lies the danger of the past and the real opportunity for better management.

It is not generally known that great numbers of bobwhites are forced to move from summer range to winter quarters. Sometimes it is only a few hundred yards. Often, however, the distance is in miles. The coveys move from the pine ridges to the hammocks in the South; from the oak lands to the fields and valleys of the Ozarks; from the prairie grasses to the thickets all over the range. On the other hand, thousands of coveys hesitate in borderline situations; enough food to be secure in November, but utterly lacking in food a month or two later. Where can they go? Nowhere with certainty. Some stumble onto new foods with cover. Others drift on in partial starvation. Many are caught in their unfamiliar surroundings.

Unfortunately, many would have us believe that the best way to avoid these drastic winter losses is to hunt the birds, killing some which are termed "surplus" because they are going to die anyhow. We must, of course, recognize that bobwhite management will produce a huntable surplus above the numbers required to replace those killed by man, animals, old age, and accidents. We need not assume, however, as many do, that the number of quail in fall will exceed our winter food supplies. More significant, we must not believe we have reached the potential carrying capacity of a tract of land as long as quail are starved to movement from summer to winter range. Unfortunately quail do not know where to go to find a winter food supply. We must take it to their summer range.

Thus we introduce a first step in land management to increase bobwhites. We need not try to grow two birds in the same coverts and food patches where only one could live last year. The easier and therefore the first objective is to grow food for a covey where no birds could exist the winter before; not forgetting, of course, the necessity to retain the coveys in their old locations, too.

The winter-food requirements of bobwhite quail are simple (Davison 1946). Quail eat many kinds of seeds but need an abundance of no more than one of essential character. In the southeast bicolor lespedeza will suffice. Corn is the staple food across the northern states, though something better might well be developed. Through the semi-arid western part of the range the grain sorghums are stalwart, but imperfect, sources of food. Soybeans support quail as long as the beans are available. The chapter on foods discusses this most important problem in more detail; it lists most of the foods you need to know about.

The point to be made here is that if they find enough food with cover throughout the winter, and the hunters don't shoot too many, the birds we began with last spring will complete a year's cycle of life, and pair off again. Sometimes it is with the same mate, more likely a different one. They need not pair with another of the same covey. Do not concern yourself with the scare-crow "in-breeding". We know of no experience suggesting the need of cross-breeding.

In any case, the coveys abandon winter quarters when the first warm days of spring appear. They begin life anew in millions of separate pairs across the range. New families are in the offing. Everyone who wants more bobwhites should ask himself "Will the lands (that I know) provide the essential things in adequate amount; so there will be more bobwhites?"

Successful management needs to provide only for the essential habits of the bobwhites.

CHAPTER V
FOOD IS THEIR GREATEST NEED

No mistake is as serious as the very common assumption that quail food is plentiful. The same fallacy is as evident in the published literature as it is in the minds of game managers, hunters and farmers. Only a few have sensed the true meaning of food sufficiency.

Food is the all important element of production. Upon food depends the vitality of the covey, its energy to feed, to escape, and to withstand the hardships of life. It is food that provides the chemical process of heat to combat the cold rains, snows, and low temperatures of winter. Food gives health and strength to overcome diseases and the life-sucking drain of red-bugs, lice, and internal parasites. Eggs in the nest must be pro-

53

duced by food. The chicks grow to maturity only if they find enough food in their daily range.

Food, never forget, is the most vital essential. It is one of the things you can do something about if you wish. Food can be produced or lost through land management. Few farms have a good supply of quail foods the whole year 'round. We cannot produce lots of quail without lots of food.

Native plants, of course, supported more than a few of the coveys in our woodland, cropland and rangeland areas throughout the bobwhite range. The birds have eaten the foods and survived in the shelter of many natural legumes, grasses, shrubs, vines and trees.

Research workers concluded from early studies of quail and their foods that the exceptional variety of foods taken was eaten as a matter of choice (Stoddard and Handley 1931). Thus, as I have stated earlier, almost everyone concerned with bobwhites accepted the principle that quail require much variety in their diet. Variety, however, is a difficult objective in land management. It also appeared to me to be an erroneous conclusion. It seemed more likely that the great variety was a result not of choice but of dire necessity due to a meagerly limited amount of each. The latter proved to be correct (Davison 1942 b). Management of food is a simpler process, and a more dependable one when variety is no longer an objective.

It was once the practice to examine quail territory and list the native legumes which were observed growing scattered in the woods; with the conclusion that all was right if the terrain was rich botanically.

To trousers covered with beggar-ticks technicians and laymen alike often point with the remark, "The woods are full of beggarweed." But are they? Seldom. Beggar-ticks usually grow thinly scattered through the woods and sedge fields. Your trousers pick up the seed more easily than a bird can do it. It is a serious mistake to ride or walk across your lands identifying a few partridge peas, perennial lespedezas, and sumacs, with the assumption "there's a plenty of food." There is seldom enough seed per square yard to feed a dozen birds well. The covey will

GROUND CONDITION FOR GOOD FEEDING
Little trash, lots of seed.

be forced to hunt for hours to find enough. Such experience does not beckon them back tomorrow. They may as well drift along elsewhere, and they usually do.

Food sufficiency must be gauged as to the *quantity of food on the land.* Moreover, only the foods which will produce every year are worthy of dependence. An abundance of quail cannot be expected in any area where food becomes scarce, even as seldom as once in four or five years. We have ample evidence that plenty of kafir corn, or maize, or soybeans, or annual lespedeza, or cowpeas, or possibly any one of a dozen others will sustain wild birds well as long as one is abundant and available.

Food availability in fall and early winter, however, is not enough. There must still be plenty in February, March, and April.

To many, availability has simply meant some seed near cover. That is not correct. A *food, to be available, must be enough to feed the covey easily,* repaying them for the energy expended. It must be free from heavy cover of stems and leaves. A thick cover of leaves, needles, or grass hides too great a percentage of the seed.

In most, if not all, of the range, insects, greens, and summer ripened seeds are more than sufficient from the time the birds pair off until the first fall frost. So summer foods are not a bothering concern of the manager. Winter foods are the first important factor in management.

Nature has a way of lulling us to sleep on this problem, producing an abundance of seeds and mast, such as acorns, grain sorghums and cowpeas, in the fall. But we must not forget that the fall abundance dwindles rapidly. It is worth repeating that livestock eat many of the plants and tramp much of the seed into the ground. Doves, sparrows, black-birds, mice, squirrels, rabbits, and dozens of small birds compete with the quail, eating many of the foods and thus reducing the supply week by week. A number of the better fall foods simply rot. Many are eaten up by worms and weevils that hatch within them. Moreover a number of foods eaten readily by bobwhites fail to mature some years.

So dependable food may be described as one which: (1) the birds eat readily, (2) is available in early fall when birds are locating for the winter, (3) is eaten but seldom by other wild creatures, (4) remains available without deterioration until summer insects appear, and (5) produces every year without fail.

You should evaluate any kind of food in which you may be interested by the way it stands up under critical scrutiny as to these five characteristics. If the plant you consider fails in any one of these five salient points, it is not an adequate quail food.

Unfortunately, we have not yet solved the winter food problem in every section of the quail range. For the southeastern states, however, we have found an outstanding plant, bicolor lespedeza, which has proven to be a highly dependable food from fall, thru winter and spring. Though you may live in a section where bicolor is not well adapted, you will be interested in the following information about this newly discovered quail-food.

BICOLOR LESPEDEZA

Bicolor lespedeza was developed by the Soil Conservation Service specifically for bobwhites. It has earned a place in the management of land in many states. Bicolor supports quail better than either nature or man has been able to do before; and bicolor can be grown permanently in certain patterns of soil conservation farming.

The seeds are taken readily by bobwhites, the bark and leaves are eaten extensively by rabbits, and the flowers are attractive to honey-bees. Bicolor is a dependable plant which will live many years without replanting. At least one plot in the south is more than 50 years old. It withstands burning, disking, cutting, or rabbit use in winter; and it will control erosion on the sites recommended. You will like its attractive appearance, too.

Bicolor is a shrub that grows 5 to 10 feet high. Its roots are perennial. The plant will leaf out along the woody stem each spring in the South as do other woody shrubs. In the North it comes anew from buds at the crown of the root. Like the other lespedezas it is a legume. Bicolor and several similar shrub lespedezas were introduced from Asia as ornamentals under names such as Oriental lespedeza and flowering desmodium. Several have slightly more showy flowers but grow fewer seed than bicolor.

The plants of common bicolor are hardy as far north as central New England, but they fail to ripen seed if frost comes before October 15. This happens too often north of the Ohio River and Virginia. Bicolor has been but partially successful in Florida. Strains, however, have been selected by the Soil Conservation Service to get a plant better adapted to various conditions. For the southern states strain 101 became the first improved strain—more vigorous and higher yielding. Several are being tested throughout the natural range of the bobwhite quail. Thus bicolor may become more successful north of the Ohio River, and in Florida. Or, equally possible, a related kind of lespedeza which ripens in early September may be the answer.

By food studies and hunting we now know that bicolor is a preferred food of quail. They eat the seeds in preference to their usual favorites—annual lespedezas, cowpeas, partridge peas, and acorns. The bobwhites begin feeding on bicolor in early fall, before the hunting season. They usually feed in the evening, often at other times of day. One will find the birds using this good food until they change to insects and the new crop of early summer seeds. Thus it measures up to all-winter and late-spring dependability.

In feeding tests of pen-reared pheasants in Pennsylvania, bicolor proved to be an excellent food. Doves eat the seed sparingly in February and March. Few if any other birds eat bicolor seed. This is fortunate for quail conservation, as it leaves the seed for the bobwhites.

Bicolor needs no defense against the criticism of those who advocate variety in their diet. Greens, insects and other seeds will be available, also, wherever you use bicolor.

Bicolor has some limitations, of course. It must be put where it won't be grazed. Cattle or horses will graze the plant

BICOLOR LESPEDEZA
(1) Woodland border; (2) flowers and leaves (3) seeded branch;
(4) seed—one in hull, three with hulls removed.

to death. Heavy concentrations of deer make establishment diffi-cult. Bicolor will not grow well on wet land. A soil conserva-tionist can be of help. He knows soils. He knows how and where to use bicolor. If bobwhite food must be grown on wet land, sesbania is used. Bicolor, however, will attract swamp coveys to upland food strips on pine or oak ridges.

The Soil Conservation Service began to use this shrub lespe-deza for wildlife and erosion control in 1935. It was used first in gullies, then on borders between woods and cropland. Food strips inside the woodland, and hedges across fields, came later.

The best ways to use bicolor are given in the chapter on wildlife land and its management.

NUTRITIOUS FOODS

The nutritional value of foods has been the subject of much speculation. A number of scientists have believed there might be nutritional significance in certain foods which are consumed only in small quantities. They theorized that some important chemical element might be hidden therein. None has come to light, and is not likely to. These small amounts of many foods in quail craws have their significance only as proof that favored foods are scarce.

Much has been learned, however, about the protein requirements of quail in captivity (Nestler et al 1944); also their need for Vitamin A (Nestler and Bailey 1943).

As far as field management is concerned, we have no evidence that proteins and vitamins are exceptional problems. Laboratory experiments have confirmed the birds' wisdom in their choice of foods (Nestler et al 1945; Edminster and Langanback 1944). Corn, bicolor lespedeza, ragweed, and insects proved highly nutritive, containing good amounts of proteins and Vitamin A. Thus by taste, or enjoyable health, the birds select what is best for them.

This seems true also in the case of poisonous and useless seeds. Quail refuse to eat the seeds of coffee-weed, crotalaria, blue lupine, and wild winter peas. The first two are violently poisonous when eaten. Seeds of the last two plants seem only to create a condition of starvation.

So bobwhite management afield may ignore vitamins and

nutritional angles if you will simply grow plenty of a good food for the birds. Consequently landowners need only simple, direct methods to produce the food we expect from land management.

THOSE FOOD-PATCH MIXTURES

Whether you live in the north or south or west, you probably have read a suggestion: "Plant a mixture of grains and legumes in your food patches for quail." The lists include: corn, kaffir, maize, buckwheat, wheat, barley, flax, millets, oats, vetch, lespedezas, sunflowers, soybeans, cowpeas, and benne—all good foods at certain times. The lists sometimes include poor foods such as sudan grass, sweet clover, broomcorn, and wild winter peas. In either case the lists are too long. They contain nonessential foods and they fail to specify the soils or locations for such plantings on the farm.

You should never plant these confounded mixtures. Find out what you need, what your soil will grow, and plant the one or two which meet the essential requirements of the bobwhites for the entire winter. Three or more plants sown in a mixture is wasted effort and doomed to disappointment.

Obviously these principles of food requirements are sometimes satisfied by residues from cropland and by native foods. Nevertheless, you will sustain no high populations without managed wildlife-land, as described in the next chapter.

Scientists have recorded more than 400 kinds of seeds eaten by bobwhites. Most of them, however, were taken in such small amounts as to be negligible (Davison 1942 b). Only a few are important. The following plants include those (in addition to bicolor lespedeza) worth knowing something about.

CROPS

Sericea. *Lespedeza sericea.* This perennial plant caused heated controversy as to food value in the early 1940's. It is a *poor* food (Davison 1945). The seed is small and hard; is eaten with the hull on. Contrary to claims that quail will not eat sericea, we have several quail craws from Georgia, South Carolina, and North Carolina which contain from 10 to 100% sericea. It is still a poor food, but useful as cover on field borders.

Annual Lespedezas. *Lespedeza striata,* and *Lespedeza stipulacea.* These include common, Korean, and Kobe. Very good foods. Used little by any other birds, though doves eat the seeds in late winter. Suitable for cropland and food patches in woods. Do not deteriorate until germination. Make seed dependably when fertilized. Not suited for western arid region, or peninsular Florida. Require neutral to acid soils. Are not successful on deep sands. Lack dependability as a food supply when grown in crop rotations because of hay-cutting, fall plowing, and change of crop which destroys seed at times when the bobwhites still need food.

Cowpeas. *Vigna sinensis.* A very good food as long as available. Grown in cropland with corn or alone. Is eaten readily by doves, deer, and rabbits. Deteriorates in warm damp weather, and often from weevils. Some strains resist deterioration. Produces seed dependably except in low rainfall belt to the west. Is seldom grown in northern states. Must be planted every summer.

Soybeans. *Soja max.* Same evaluation as for cowpeas. Is grown in both northern and southern states. Almost impossible to grow where deer are frequent, as it is a preferred food of deer.

Mung Beans. *Phaseolus mungo.* This is a small bean quite

palatable to the bobwhites (Nestler 1949). May be grown very much as cowpeas and soybeans; but it is an annual which must be planted again every year.

Florida Beggarweed. *Desmodium purpureum*. A good food produced abundantly in cornfields in Florida and the southern third of South Carolina, Georgia, Alabama, and Mississippi. Does not produce seed farther north. Suitable only for cropland. Nothing else eats the seed. Will reseed itself, once established. The seed is the smallest of the foods rating fair or better.

Sesbania. *Sesban macrocarpa*. A fair food. Nothing else eats it. Grows best on wet lands, too wet for other cultivated crops. Produces a heavy crop of seed in the coastal areas of South Carolina, Georgia, Florida, Alabama, Mississippi, Louisiana, and Texas. Will not ripen farther north. A second species, *S. exaltata* is fairly common in Texas. Does not deteriorate. Does not drop its seed until December. Perhaps the best plant for wet soils. Will reseed. Ground should be disked in February or March. Suitable for food strips in woodland, and wet field borders. A fall food such as browntop millet or bull grass must be grown with it to feed the birds until mid-winter.

Browntop Millet. Texas Millet. *Panicum ramosum, P. texanus*. Good foods in late summer and early fall. Many kinds of birds eat the seeds, including doves and turkeys. Suitable for cropland. Best used in combination with sesbania. The two together cover the winter season. Alone, millets fail to carry the birds through the winter.

Grain Sorghums—Kafir, maize, hegari. Good foods. Important in semi-arid portions at western edge of range. Suitable for cropland. Blackbirds, doves, ducks, deer, mice, and most all birds and animals eat them also, thus denying quail the abundance needed. Deteriorate badly in the humid areas.

Corn. The best food for northern areas. Pheasants, squirrels, raccoons, and rodents compete severely. Suitable for cropland. Should be available all the time—not just in emergency storm periods.

Wheat, Oats, Rye, Barley. Good foods, seldom important due to poor availability. Competition of all other animals severe as with sorghums—suitable for cropland.

Vetch. *Vicia spp.* Augusta vetch, V. *augustifolia* is a very good food for quail and doves. Suitable for cropland with small grain. Will not deteriorate. Requires fertile land. Ripens April and May. An annual.

Benne. *Sesamum indicum.* Not important for quail. Difficult to grow, suitable at best only on cropland.

Crotalaria. Several species are now used in agriculture. Quail eat none of them though they seed abundantly. This plant was once sold for quail food.

Blue Lupine. *Lupinus augustifolius.* A new winter legume in the Deep South. Quail do not eat it. A variety of "sweet lupine" might prove edible.

Caley Peas. *Lathyrus hirsutus.* A winter legume, something like vetch used in the Deep South. Quail do not eat it.

Buckwheat is definitely over-rated for southern use. May be important in northern bobwhite management. An annual which fails to control erosion on sloping land.

Peanuts are eaten by quail but cannot be considered an important food due to the winter bareness of peanut fields. Doves find peanuts more important. Quail cannot live through the winter on peanuts as they are grown in cropland.

Note: A perennial plant is more desirable than an annual for quail management. Annuals must be reestablished every year; and cultivation for this purpose causes considerable soil erosion. Annual planting is also more expensive—and less dependable.

WEEDS OF CROPLAND

Pokeberry. *Phytolacca americana.* A fair food with good possibilities. Livestock do not eat it. A perennial, may have value in wildlife hedges, particularly in fences of multiflora rose. A preferred food of doves.

Ragweed. *Ambrosia elatior,* A. *psilostachya.* A very good quail food. Also eaten readily by doves and all other seed eating birds. Grows with small grain in fields, remaining in idle fields a year or two. Also in overgrazed pastures. The giant ragweed, A. *trifida* is not a good food.

Sunflowers. *Helianthus spp.* A very good quail food in the west. Also preferred by doves and all other seed eating birds. Grows in idle fields two or three years after cultivation in western fourth of quail range. Does not deteriorate in semi-arid climate. An annual.

Bull Grass. *Paspalum boscianum.* The best of the paspalums. Eaten also by doves and other seed-eating birds. A weed of the corn fields in southern half of the range. Does not deteriorate. An annual. May be the best plant with sesbania for wet coastal lands. Both volunteer with spring disking.

Dove Weed, Goat Weed, Texas Croton. *Croton capitata,* C. *texanus,* C. *glandulosus,* and other species. Fair foods in late summer and fall. Also favorite food of doves. Grow in overgrazed pastures; follow small grains; and also grow a year or two on idle cropland. Deteriorate moderately. Reseeding annuals.

Pigweed. *Amaranthus spp.* A fair food. Seeds small. Grows in rich spots of idle land. Not important. Annual.

Chocolate Weed. *Riedlea hirsuta.* A fair food. Grows in wet land, where soil has been disturbed by disking or otherwise. Native to coastal South Carolina and Florida. Not important. Annual.

Yellow Foxtail. *Setaria lutescens.* A fair food. Possibly important in northern states. Eaten by many other birds. Annual.

TREES AND SHRUBS

Oak Acorns. *Quercus spp.* A good food. Eaten also by squirrels, bluejays and hogs. Deteriorated rapidly by insects. A stalwart food in early winter. Not dependable in late winter and spring. Fails about 1 year out of 6.

Sweet Gum. *Liquidambar styraciflua.* A good food, also eaten by doves and many other seed eating birds. Serves well until midwinter. Makes seed every year.

Pine Mast. *Pinus spp.* Good foods but seldom available. Produce enough seed for a good supply of food only about one year in 3 to 7. Doves and rodents eat the seed readily. Germinate by February.

Flowering Dogwood. *Cornus florida.* The skins are eaten. Fair food. Fruits most years. Of secondary importance.

Black Locust. *Robinia pseudoacacia.* A fair food. Produces most every year. Might be important in western part of range.

Ash, Pecans, Sassafras, Maple, Osage Orange, Beech, Black Cherry, Black Gum. Eaten but not important generally.

Blackberry. *Rubus spp.* Good summer food. Produces every year. Appears to be an unnecessary delicacy as many coveys live well beyond reach of blackberries, mulberries, or any other fruit.

Honeysuckle. *Lonicera japonica.* Eaten—but perhaps important only when snow or other conditions make food supplies scarce. A bitter fruit, also eaten by some other birds. An excellent cover plant.

Sumac. *Rhus glabra, R. copallina.* Eaten but not important.

Poison Ivy. *Rhus radicans.* Eaten but not important.

Wax Myrtle. *Myrica cerifera, M. caroliniana.* A fair food in Florida and the Gulf Coast. Unimportant in the main range of the bobwhite. Important in pastures of peninsular Florida, particularly. Cattle do not graze it.

Gall Berry. *Ilex glabra.* A fair food, particularly in woodland pastures of Florida and South Georgia. A bitter fruit used in late winter by mocking birds and others.

Sparkleberry. *Vaccineum arboreum.* Eaten occasionally but probably unimportant.

The following shrubs and trees are *not* important as foods for bobwhites. The fruits are rarely eaten (Davison 1942 b):

Wild Rose, *Rosa spp.*

Wild Grape, *Vitis spp.*

Red Cedar, *Juniperus virginiana.*

Red Bud, *Cercis canadensis.*

Beauty Berry, *Callicarpa americana.*

Coral Berry, *Symphoricarpos orbiculatus.*

Virginia Creeper, *Parthenocissus quinquefolia.*

Smilax or Cat-Briar, *Smilax spp.*

WILD HERBS IN WOODLAND OR IDLE LAND

Partridge Pea. *Chamaecrista fasciculata, C. nictitans, C. spp.* A good food. Produces seed most years. Quail turn from it to other foods in March if possible. More important in black-belt of Alabama than elsewhere, except Florida. Fires keep partridge peas in productive conditions in woods. Not eaten by other birds. Annuals.

Beggartick. *Desmodium spp.* A good food though usually scattered thinly. Grows in open woods and idle fields. Yields seed every year. There are more than a dozen of these plants, all perennials except the Florida beggarweed which grows in cropland. In the perennial species lie possibilities of development for land management, though to date efforts by Stoddard, the Soil Conservation Service, and several states have not yielded enough to be satisfactory.

Milk Peas. *Galactia spp.* A good food. Grows almost unseen in the woods on a tender twining vine. Management unknown. A perennial. Does not deteriorate while needed.

Butterfly Peas. *Centrosema virginiana.* A good food. Less abundant than milk peas. A perennial. Does not deteriorate while needed.

Jewel Weed. *Impatiens spp.* A good food, though limited to wet lands, principally in Virginia. An annual. The management of this plant is little known.

Wild Beans. *Strophostyles umbellata, S. helvola,* and *S. pauciflora.* All are eaten. The first is more common. These grow only on idle land—a condition that promises little for their future use. Weevils are often bad in *S. helvola.*

Nut-Rushes. *Scleria spp.* A main food in peninsular Florida and in the Gulf Coast counties of Mississippi. A grass-like plant (actually a sedge) of wet lands. Will not deteriorate easily.

The following common plants, sometimes thought useful as bobwhite foods, are not important.

Bush Clovers, perennial *Lespedeza spp.*

Johnson Grass, *Sorghum halepense.*

Crab Grass, *Digitaria sanguinalis.*

Marsh Elder, *Iva ciliata.*

Rough Buttonweed, *Diodia teres.*

Morning Glory, *Ipomoea spp.*

Giant Ragweed, *Ambrosia trifida.*

Chickweed, *Alsine media.*

Smartweed, *Persicaria spp.*

Mexican Clover, pursley, *Richardia scabra.*

The seeds of another 300 plants are eaten occasionally but none of them are important enough to consider (Davison 1942 b).

CHAPTER VI
COVER, TOO, IS ESSENTIAL

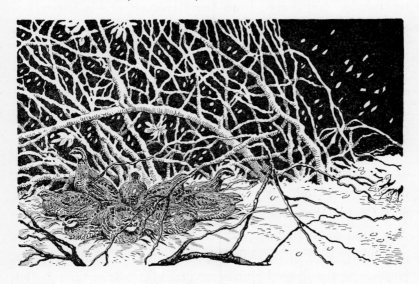

The cover needs of bobwhites are also less complex than most people believe. Yet, food alone will not support quail. They must have shelter in which to live. Call it "shelter", "cover", or "covert" as you wish.

Several publications recommend a long list of shrubs and vines to plant for quail cover. They should be revised, simplified. Most authors and lecturers describe several kinds of protective cover—roosting, resting, loafing, nesting, emergency, escape— and travel lanes of cover. Cover is more simple than these several terms imply.

Quail need two kinds of cover—grassy and shrubby. The grass and woody plants may be any of several kinds. We learned this lesson beyond question in 1943, when 38 strips of bicolor

were planted beside various kinds of cover on Belmont Planta-
tion, Hampton County, South Carolina. To our surprise, quail
used every strip the first year, and thereafter. Cover alongside
the bicolor food ranged from heavy thickets of blackberry and
plum to open broomsedge fields and scattered pines. Some were
next to cotton fields on one side, thinly scattered pine and grass
cover on the other. (Brushy cover, however, existed within flying
distance—one quarter of a mile—of every strip). These early
observations have been verified on dozens of Georgia and South
Carolina preserves since 1943.

Quail use the grass cover for roosting at night and resting
in midday; they scatter into it when hunted by men, dogs, or
wild animals. Under its protective blades, the parents make their
nest. Grass is the ground cover for quail.

Wild plum thickets protect thousands of coveys of quail,
particularly west of the Mississippi River. This plant is useless,
however, if the natural grasses are grazed from the thicket. It is
the grass that holds body warmth against wind and cold. It is
the plum branch that apparently gives overhead assurance against
attack.

In the eastern part of the range, blackberry and honeysuckle
vie for promience as the leading shrub cover for quail. Even a
bird dog can hardly disturb the birds in these two types of cover.
Honeysuckle is particularly comforting during rain and snow,
the nearly ever-green leaves being responsible. Unlike plum and
blackberry which have no winter food value, honeysuckle berries
are eaten; though sparingly perhaps because they are very bitter.

Any swamp has cover aplenty in the South, regardless of the
woody species present. The sawtooth palmetto of southern pastures and woodland gives adequate cover for birds to escape, also
for shade and protection against rains.

In northern areas, evergreens and tall grasses and weeds provide the savior-cover against ordinary storms. Unfortunately research workers have not isolated the plants which provide "essential cover" to protect the covey through the killer-storms. Perhaps the investigators have not considered the need for simple essentials in northern cover, as Errington, Frye, and others pointed to one essential food, corn. Multiflora rose, recently developed in Missouri, Illinois, and northeastern states looks promising as a cover plant. Yet, these rose plantings need added cover; grass, at least; and perhaps evergreens, too.

Cover, like food, must be placed carefully and sparingly into your patterns of land use. You can have too much cover. And you can have too much open land without cover. No farm's economy will stand a reckless distribution of grass and shrubs. So be carefully efficient with your cover designs.

Thus in simplest terms: Cover must provide nesting sites, warmth at the ground level, and overhead protection against aerial attack. Cover must be near the food supply.

The theme of the following chapters is simplicity of land management to provide the food and cover needed to support millions of coveys. *Emphasis is on the essentials:* In other words, the usable practices that a landowner can apply.

CHAPTER VII
WILDLIFE LAND AND ITS MANAGEMENT

If you want quail in abundance, you will reckon with "wildlife land," interspersed wherever you can afford it in fields, woods, and pastures. Wildlife land is land which is managed and reserved for the sole purposes of the game you intend to produce. For bobwhites the areas need not be large.

Land management for quail is not new. Owners of a few plantations and hunting preserves have expended much effort with varying degrees of success since the close of the 19th century. One variant never attained was to be able to grow enough birds.

The chief problems of management are: (1) which foods, (2) what cover, and (3) where shall each be located on a man's

land? Where to provide them influences the kinds of food you
select and the cover which can be made available. Thus we must
carefully inquire into the landowner's wishes. We must look at
his land with him and consider his plans for managing it; for,
remember, bobwhites must find the food and shelter they need
within each farm, or you do not have successful management.

Quail management, pursued only as a by-product of cropland, woodland, and pasture management, is not as effective as
we had all hoped through recent years. Whether it's Florida,
Texas, Michigan or New York you will find much of the land is
quail-less for lack of food or cover or both. No laws, no restocking, no sportsmanship can alleviate these faults of habitat. The
only solution is to add the essential elements which are lacking.
It is as simple as that. And it is not expensive.

The economic need to wrest some financial return from
every foot of land is not as formidable a barrier against inclusion
of wildlife land in farm patterns, as many despairing wildlifers
have lamented. Where measures for the restoration of bobwhites
are properly fitted to the land, bobwhites will thrive in greater
numbers than heretofore.

Wildlife land was recognized only recently as a sound use
of land in patterns of farm and timber management (Davison
1942 a). There are really two types of wildlife land.

First, there is land that has no other economic use: stream
banks, eroded and sapped field borders, spoil banks, and other
odd areas. These bits of land were never profitable when used
for field crops, trees, pasture, or hay. Insofar as these areas occur
on your land, you should make them produce cover or food, or
both, for bobwhites.

Second, wildlife land is a use often wanted on land which is also suitable for crops, woods, or pasture. When you decide to use small areas of these kinds of land for wildlife, you will want to grow food; lots of food; the best food that can be produced on very small strips of land—not too small, just enough. If you do not have sufficient cover immediately beside your food-strip, you must provide the shelter, too. Again as little as possible—but enough.

When you grow quail foods and quail cover anywhere, you will want to be certain of three things: (1) that the plants you use are the best for the purpose, (2) that your wildlife lands are in a correct pattern with the adjoining lands, and (3) that you keep down the acreage of land to be managed to the least amount possible for success.

I have made the point emphatically that winter quail food is seldom sufficient in nature or man's recent management of land. Bicolor lespedeza is astonishingly successful on lands where everyone once believed the food supply was abundant, and also on "poor lands" where quail abundance seemed impossible. The discovery and development of bicolor permitted simplification of management. It gave us new concepts—new principles—in bobwhite management. Bicolor makes excellent use of wildlife land; it provides food abundance when planted in correct land-use patterns.

WHERE TO GROW BICOLOR

Bicolor may be grown in woods, on borders, across broomsedge fields, or near vegetated stream banks without more cover than it provides itself. We may find it necessary to add some cover to bicolor hedges across fields in cultivation. If bicolor is ever grown in pastures, it will probably be between two living fences of multiflora rose.

The pattern of planting is important. The best economy is to use land that is not needed for other purposes. Or if it is necessary to use good land for game, grow a lot of food on a little land. This may take 1 percent of a woodland; 3 percent of a field in borders; or 5 percent of cultivated land in hedges. The remaining 99, 97, or 95 percent of the land should be made to produce excellent crops or woodland products.

When we try to guarantee enough food for our birds by managing only 1 percent or 2 percent of our land, we must manage the small bits of land to produce as much food as possible. Fifty pounds of seed scattered over 10 acres are almost useless— lost in 400 thousand square feet of space. An equal amount (50 pounds of seed) on a strip one-eighth acre in size sets a good table for the birds. Less than one-eighth acre will not feed a covey well. Since good care is worth while, you should prepare the land well, plant carefully, fertilize enough to promote excellent growth, and cultivate if necessary to keep the bicolor free of weeds, grass, and trees. The same principle will hold for any other food plant.

One objective is to grow the bicolor without grasses underneath. A vigorous growth of bicolor, once started, usually will shade out all other vegetation between the rows. The seeds then fall only among the bicolor leaves where the birds find them quickly by scratching. Even bicolor seeds that fall in heavy grass are not attractive.

Bicolor can be established with one-year nursery-grown plants or by planting seed. Plants are more expensive but more dependable than seed. Yet plants cost less than ordinary food patches of cowpeas, millets, and other annuals. The same strip does not have to be planted again next year. Nor is there the risk next spring of the weather being either too wet or too dry at planting time. So regardless of the way the strips are established, the perennial bicolor is economical and dependable as a food for bobwhites.

The width of a good bicolor strip is important. Less than 12 feet is too narrow, produces too little. More than 20 feet is too wide, making bird-dog work and shooting a disappointment. A width of 15 to 18 feet is best; hunting is a pleasure, dogs work beautifully, and birds have enough food.

FOOD STRIPS IN WOODLAND

Bicolor food strips deserve very wide application in openings of southern pineland and blackjack. They will attract the coveys as soon as the seed is produced. The number of strips to grow on each 100 acres has not yet been determined, but is important. One strip for each 20 or 25 acres is conservative. Perhaps one for each 10-acre tract is none too many. We need not think of more than this until further results are measured in terms of quail per strip. Four or five bicolor strips per 100 acres of woods will feed four or five coveys well. Openings large enough for a food strip are common in much of the woodland in the South.

A length of 400 feet is good. Perhaps 300 is enough. We have found two and three coveys on longer strips, but there the dogs often range too far ahead of the hunter. Furthermore, long strips either take up too much land or leave too much space between strips. So 15- to 18-foot plantings 400 feet long appear, now, to be the best design. This will be about one-eighth acre and should produce 30 to 60 pounds of seed per strip, as long as it is cared for well. Since it is a perennial, this means year after year, indefinitely. This standard strip requires 800 to 1,000 plants or one to two pounds of seed.

The same design should be used in old fields of broomsedge or brush, as in woodland. If the woods or broomsedge is burned, allow the fire to burn the bicolor, too. The bicolor will not be harmed.

Bicolor is also an excellent plant for highway fills, dikes, and spoil banks in or near woodland. For example, the big dikes of the Santee-Cooper reservoirs in South Carolina had serious erosion. Grasses were too shallow-rooted to hold well. Moreover, this steep man-made land had no value for grazing, hay, or woodland. Bicolor successfully controlled the erosion and gave the land its only possible use—the production and conservation of more quail. Any dirt fill or spoil bank can be made useful with bicolor. Quail feed daily on highway fills covered with bicolor near Sandy Level, Virginia. The traffic is atop the road and hidden by its shoulder, disturbing the feeding birds none at all. It is not good on highway cuts.

The wasted land beneath power lines and telephone wires through southern woodlands can be brought to use through bicolor. This treatment of land is compatible with economy of maintenance. Here, again, has been potential wildlife-land waiting only for this advancement in practical science of land use and management to include wildlife conservation.

BORDERS

Field borders along woodlands, streams, and gullies are excellent places to locate food for bobwhites. Cover is already

provided in the shrubs and grass of the adjoining land. In the
South, particularly, field borders are sapped by trees at the edge
of the field; crops are not profitable in an area of 30 feet or more
out from the trees; and erosion is a severe problem. This land
has no use except for wildlife food and cover. To withstand the
competition of the living tree roots, a perennial plant having a

WILDLIFE BORDER IN PLACE

similar root-system is more dependable than annuals which must
grow anew from seeds each year. Bicolor, and in some places
sericea lespedeza, have proven most useful for borders.

Bicolor borders, we think, should extend the full length of
the woodland-cropland edge, since this land has no other use.
Hunting at the woodland edge will be rough compared to open-
field and open-woodland shooting; but you can have more quail
by improvement of borders.

The border of bicolor should be 12 to 20 feet wide. If crop-
rows run into the border, a 12- to 15-foot strip of sericea lespedeza will be needed for turning between the bicolor and the

crop. Sericea is a poor food but a good ground cover for the birds. Bobwhites will be found resting by day and roosting at night in sericea, particularly if they have no grassy cover in the woods. Quail do not rest or roost in bicolor in winter. They go there only to feed. Its cover is sufficient for safe feeding.

HEDGES AND WINDBREAKS

The windbreaks of the western and northern sections of the quail range offer obvious shelter against the blizzards of winter and early spring. They are thus closely akin to wildlife land. Their fault is: food shortage. Those shocks of corn or something else dependable are necessary if you really want bobwhites in good number.

Hedges of bicolor in crop fields of the South are new. We are not yet sure that they are worth the land they occupy. Strips 12 to 15 feet wide (4 or 5 rows) will take about 5% of the land if grown 300 feet apart. They must go all the way across the field to join cover at one end or both. We believe one hedge will support another as added cover. The crops grown between the hedges should be different, perhaps, where the rotation makes such an arrangement possible. Don't try these hedges until use of all borders has been made and strips put inside the woodland. We may find it necessary to add stronger cover to these bicolor hedges, but for the present bicolor is being tried alone.

The greatest problem about cover is: How to have it in or around open fields—and pastures? There are many who will say "You simply can't afford it." But perhaps you can!

There are landowners who want birds very keenly. If narrow hedges spaced across the field will increase their birds decidedly, they can well afford to farm with hedge designs. As just pointed out, this invasion of the old "clean farming" school is new and none-too-well proven. But it has some exciting possibilities. And in much of the more level prairie states, thousands of fields totalling millions of acres will remain quail-less unless satisfactory hedge patterns are developed.

Hedges around fields—and across them—are more than an

SHRUB HEDGES ACROSS CROPLAND

idealist's dream. England and France and other older countries are criss-crossed with living fences and boundary hedges. Early American hedges of osage orange supported much game while they were in vogue. True, the osage orange hedge is passing from the American farm scene; but into modern farm patterns is coming the living fence of multiflora rose. It is a plant of beauty and economic service which does not rob the adjacent land of its crop productivity. First demonstrated by the Soil Conservation Service in the early 1940's, the rose fence flashes a vision of new patterns to come. Hedges are here to stay; are here to be improved, developed, and increased vastly.

Remember the proposition that we must outdo our earlier concept of conservation, limited to "saving". We must *produce* more game if we want good hunting. And we can well afford to consider hedges in the light of that idea.

Let those who "cannot afford" hedges continue without birds across their fields. To those who like to pioneer, I say: "Try a series of hedges. Help us develop a hedge of such high quality that thousands of those who now believe they cannot afford such intensive game management will come to accept the idea and apply it."

The hedge is the most promising method of taking cover into open land. I do not believe in "travel lanes" for quail. Bobwhites should not be made to travel from cover to cover—or from cover to food. Both should be maintained side-by-side. A hedge should supply not only the food but the cover for roosting, resting, nesting, and escape. The latter need may dictate a series of hedges which support each other. All of us have seen coveys, flushed at one end of a hedge, alight in the same hedge a little farther away. Why not extend their range to other hedges a hundred yards or so on either side?

The quail hunter's horizons need not be as limited as our present experience. How far we can go is yet to be determined. How far do you want to go?

If the sport of quail hunting is worth only a dollar and a quarter license annually, you have probably hunted much more in the past than you will in the future. If it is worth two or three dollars a covey, you can afford to keep your gun and considerable hope. For those who can afford a hundred dollars or more a year —and a lot of people can—intensive land management holds lots of promise.

You might think offhand that too much prominence has been given to bicolor lespedeza and multiflora rose as food and cover, to be planted on wildlife land for bobwhites. Their significance is hard to exaggerate. They are more dependable than any other plants in the range to which they are adapted. Bicolor gave us positive proof of natural food deficiencies. It taught us new, simpler, and more successful principles of bobwhite management. The value of any other food plant can be measured best by comparing its characteristics with bicolor lespedeza. Bobwhites, themselves, and hundreds of landowners supplied the evidence for the above conclusions. Bicolor is worthy of a trial wherever quail exist. I am sure it will require a drought resistant strain for the west, an early ripening strain for the north. If these cannot be developed, bobwhite management will remain unsatisfied until someone discovers something else of equal character.

CHAPTER VIII
WOODLAND MANAGEMENT

Woodland can be favorable or unfavorable for bobwhites. Grazed woodlands are very poor, almost useless for the ground-living birds. In the North, *ungrazed* woodlands give material protection against blizzard conditions. In the South, much of the pine woods is burned annually and, surprising as it may be, has provided some of the best quail areas. Generally, the growth condition of woodlands is too heavy for bobwhites. Management can make the woods more suitable.

Forest is the logical crop for 56 percent of the entire land area of the 13 southern states, according to the most recent report of the Southern Association of Science and Industry. Southern quail managers, then, may well reckon with woodland practices favorable to bobwhites. The Southern Association also points out that 132 million acres of the total 195 million in southern woods is owned and operated privately. Thus more than two-thirds of the opportunity for quail conservation with woodland is a problem of private land management. It involves 1,839,000 separate owners.

It is pertinent to recognize that problems which are inherent with cropland are no barriers to woodland management. Though the northwestern area of bobwhite range is less wooded than the southeastern states, any farm containing several acres of woods has opportunities for quail management.

The natural foods in woodland, however, are far from adequate for quail. The value of ordinary woodland management has been exaggerated as a beneficial factor to bobwhites. On the other hand, many people have believed you could not produce high populations of quail in woodlands. The best covey range was once believed to require four environmental types—woodland, brushland, grassland, and cultivation—in close proximity (Leopold, 1931). It was also believed that the highest quail populations could only be produced if woodland sections were broken by cropland equal to about 25 percent of the woods (Stoddard, 1931). Bobwhite requirements are neither so exacting nor difficult to provide. Ground cover plus adequate food will suffice.

To have enough food for quail in or near woodlands, we may consider three ways of producing it:

1. *The supplementary foods of adjacent cropland*, which are sometimes sufficient. This food supply, however, is rarely dependable.

2. *Fire* which has supplied considerable foods in southern pinelands and burned-over oak ridges throughout the range.

Our present concept is that these annually-burned woodlands were far less sufficient in foods than we once believed. There is no doubt, however, that burned woods have fed quail much better than unburned woodlands.

3. *The management of wildlife lands* at woodland borders and within the interior. This is the most dependable means to guarantee an abundant supply of food. Thus wildlife land, in the amount of about 1 percent, is the economical way to grow a good number of bobwhites in timber land.

In other words, to have good quail populations in the wooded parts of a farm or timber holding, you add the best food adapted to your section of the range. The pattern of growing food in woodland is important. Actually it calls for the judicious use of wildlife land, in borders and food strips as described in the foregoing chapter.

Wildlife borders should be used at all woodland edges. In the South, bicolor is the best food for borders. For northern conditions, shocks of corn may be the best.

Pine ridges, recently recognized as naturally poor feeding grounds (Davison 1946), generally provide excellent nesting areas in an abundance of summer foods—insects. For lack of winter food (no doubt influenced by low fertility) the birds moved back to the hammocks along the streams, often a mile or two away. (Stoddard 1931).

Management can come to the rescue. A single well-fertilized strip of good food (one-eighth acre in size) makes the ridge habitable the year 'round. Bicolor lespedeza when supported by fertilizer has proven its ability to hold quail in exactly this situation. It failed when fertility was allowed to go down to the point where it made no seed. Thus good management prevents a "fall shuffle"; supports birds and hunting where none existed the winters before; and makes areas of poorer soils a most promising opportunity for bobwhite development, well away from the discouraging problems of improved pasture and intensive crop management. Oak ridges respond to similar management.

The significance of managing no more than 1 percent of the land intensively, to effect high populations of quail over woodland areas, must be evident. One acre of the food-managed land supports 50 quail or more if distributed sensibly through the woods.

Soil Conservationists use a system of land classification which shows the ability of every soil and slope to be used profitably in accordance with known principles of good land conservation (Graham 1947). Land primarily suitable for woodland, within the natural range of the bobwhite quail, totals more than 200 million acres. Many more acres, though economically feasible for cropland and pasture, will likely remain in an equally profitable state of woodland production. Here the welfare of bobwhites can be assured by management; or allowed to deteriorate for want of it. The addition of strips of wildlife land to provide food assures success.

Such a program is sound because it assigns a negligible percentage of land to wildlife use; keeps cost of establishment and maintenance low; and supplies an essential, dependable food in enough quantity to hold birds in an area formerly uninhabited. Thus we can make use of the insects, green leaves, and scant supplies of seeds, mast and fruit which exist at times within the once-unbalanced range.

As pointed out earlier, no grazing should be permitted in woodland where quail production is wanted. Livestock eat almost every plant that produces good quail-food.

As we consider the management of only 1 percent as wild-life-land in the woods, let's also plan to make the remaining 99 percent the most productive woodland possible. It would be foolish to shy, as some have done, from wildlife usage of so small an acreage; while the entire woods is allowed to produce a fourth, a third, or half a crop of trees as so much of our wood-land is now doing.

TO PLANT NEW WOODLANDS FOR QUAIL

Bobwhites can be assured on several million acres of land which will be planted or allowed to seed naturally to trees; or the birds can be very, very scarce on these new woodland tracts —depending on the method (design and materials) applied. You must plant permanent food strips for the birds if you want them. In short, you will plant only 99 percent of the areas in trees, and 1 percent (properly distributed) with perennial bird-food such as bicolor lespedeza.

The opportunities are extensive. For example, farmers in Tennessee estimated (in 1947) that no less than 500,000 acres of their lands in that state alone were best suited for pine trees; to better employ the idle land, poor pasture, and lands which are no longer profitable as cropland due to gullies, severe sheet erosion, slope, and soil type. For this job the farmers expect to obtain and plant 600 million pine trees by purchase and grants from the state forestry nurseries over a period of approximately 20 years. These 500,000 acres, however, will support few quail if trees are planted or allowed to seed naturally in a solid pattern of woodland.

To have 20 thousand coveys of quail (250,000 birds) in these farm woodlands would require only a slight change of plans. Thirty-six million (36,000,000) bicolor lespedeza plants, substituted for only 6 million of the trees would provide winter food for these quarter-of-a-million bobwhites. As in old woodland 1,000 plants per strip, each strip four or five rows wide, will make a useful planting of about one-eighth acre. One strip of bicolor should be planted in each 10 to 20 acres of new woodland.

The individual farm owners or the state game department can be expected to purchase or produce the plants. Fifty thousand pounds of seed would successfully serve the same purpose. (To keep this example in proper perspective, you will be interested to know that 500,000 acres of proposed woodland for Tennessee is only 3 percent of the farmlands in that state.)

The important things to remember are: first, when planting the trees leave three rows unplanted for a distance of about 400 feet; second, plant the perennial bird food at the same time. This design is practical in the southeastern states where bicolor is known to be the successful plant for these strips of bird food. Similarly useful plants will no doubt be developed for the North and West.

CHAPTER IX
THE PLACE OF FIRE

Two schools of thought have conflicting beliefs regarding the use or prevention of fire in woodland. Across the northern half of the quail range, nearly unanimous opinion says in effect, "Do not allow fire in woodland under any circumstances. Unburned woods produce wildlife. Fires destroy both woods and game."

Throughout the southern sections of the range, many believe fire is an absolute necessity to production of quail in woodland. Foresters are beginning to think managed fire is profitable for tree production, too. Southern opinion has never been unanimous. Perhaps the last word has not been said yet relative to the place of fire in woodland, and even in pasture management.

93

Stoddard (1931 and 1939) recommended burning of southeastern woodland to produce the best quail hunting. First, he pointed out that fire has value as an agent of food production. Wild legumes are undoubtedly more abundant on most land which is burned every year or two. An important result of fire is the reduction of old pine needles, tree leaves, and dead grasses which drastically hide seeds from the birds in unburned woodland. Both of these reasons are facts beyond controversy.

In spite of this food value in burning, we find now that we can supply more than enough winter food for an equal number of bobwhites in a simpler, less costly way. Four or five strips of bicolor, totaling less than one acre, feed four or five coveys of birds in winter better than 100 acres of burned-over pineland.

Stoddard's further reason for burning was to keep underbrush down for open shooting. In many places brush control is absolutely necessary if you want to shoot quail. On the other hand there are large tracts of pineland where fire is seldom necessary to control underbrush. The trouble with fire is that almost no one has used it without a considerable reduction in timber production. Nevertheless there is a value in fire for trees, as insurance against worse fire.

The most surprising information to commend the use of fire comes from a publication issued by authority of the Secretary of Agriculture with the cooperation of the Association of Land-Grant Colleges and Universities (Greene 1935).

Greene points out that burning in southern Mississippi *increases organic matter 1.6 times in the soils to a depth of 6 inches,* due to a greater root development of legumes and herbs. *Nitrogen is also increased 1.5 times.* Leaving or removing the decaying organic matter above ground has no effect on the nitrogen and organic matter in the soil. It is root development that makes the difference. Greene's eight-year study revealed no differences in moisture contents of the soil between burned and unburned woodlands.

Furthermore, erosion is not affected to any significant degree by fire in southern woodlands. This was borne out by experiments conducted by the Soil Conservation Service (Copley 1944). The loss of three tons of soil per acre annually (from a 10 percent slope) was far less than occurred under the best cropland management. We may conclude that losses would have been still less under normal burning, as the plot under this experiment was burned twice a year with a blowtorch. No actual woodland burning is half so severe. Fire used with moderate care will cause only negligible erosion, particularly on the flatter sandy acres of the coastal plains.

Our worst problems facing us in the use of woodland fire come from two things: First, our woods are uneven—a few acres of pines only one to five years old; another area of trees 5 to 15 years of age; and other sections older—all in the same woods. *Fire doesn't treat these various ages alike.* Second, the common type of fires is too severe, and few people know how to handle fires right. Of the numerous preserve owners who tried to follow the kind of burning Stoddard recommended, few if any did a commendable job. I don't know all the preserves but I am well acquainted with many of them.

The United States Forest Service (Bickford and Newcomb, 1947) has developed techniques of burning which look as safe as total fire exclusion, allowing each a small margin of loss by accidents. They call it "prescribed burning", whereas Stoddard referred to his methods as "controlled burning."

The Forest Service objective is twofold: First, to reduce the hazard of serious fires, and second, to convert the composition of a forest stand from less valuable hardwood trees to the much-wanted southern pines. Pines of the South withstand some fire with negligible harm. Since they are more fire-resistant than any other trees, the fire gives landowners a method of selectivity—should they choose pines as the crop they wish to grow.

To burn successfully—which means with no more than slight damage—one must gain experience with dependable means of controlling fire. There is more to it than just keeping the flames on your own place. To manage it correctly costs considerable effort—a few men, firelanes, and an eye to the weather.

Whether you follow Stoddard's methods or those of the Forest Service, the weather is your chief ally at the time of burning—and it is your worst enemy if you allow fire at the wrong time. You never set fire when the countryside is extremely dry: The fire burns too greedily then. In other words the fire encounters too little restraint when conditions are dry.

The Forest Service plan calls for firelanes running east and west every one-eighth to one-quarter of a mile. Thus the land is cut into several separate units. They suggest that you arrange for weather forecasts, especially of wind direction; for they set their fires on the south edge of each unit so they will burn against a steady wind from the north. These backfires burn at a rate of about one foot per minute—60 to 75 feet per hour.

"Good burning conditions are found," say the foresters, "when there is a 3- to 10-mile northerly wind in clear weather immediately after rain." Wind direction is commonly variable previous to rainfall as the weather is unsettled then. Shifts in wind direction cause flankfires, or even headfires which result in greater fire intensity.

Longleaf is the most fire-resistant of the pines. Loblolly stands lots of fire, too, but less than longleaf. Slash pine should never be burned until the trees are above six feet tall when a backfire will not harm them materially. When the slash and other pines are four inches or more in diameter at breast height, a flankfire can be used safely. Flankfires are cheaper than backfires, and do no more damage to pines of 4-inch and larger diameters.

If you have areas of young pines too small to burn, protect them until they reach a self-protective size.

A number of landowners want to use fire in their pinelands and are no longer interested in turpentine operations. They simply cut the "faced" trees into pulpwood, leaving only the "round" trees which fire usually will not harm. A tree which has been faced for turpentining catches fire easily and is one of the spectacles which cause exaggerated fear of southern fires.

The neatest trick in the Forest Service method of burning is the way they set the fires. They use a fire-setting can with a long quarter-inch tube, pinched nearly together at the end so that liquid fuel is poured out in a fine but continuous stream as fast as a man can walk. The thin ribbon of fire which follows the fire-setter's line sets an even flame every inch of the way. One or two "mop-up" crewmen follow along behind. Danger is soon past because the fire is set close to the prepared firelane, and the thoroughness of the fuel-line method leaves no combustible material to catch fire later. This is a great time-saver.

An appraisal of fire damage after a burn is worth while, and may be a good guide to the next year's job. "When the tree crowns are not scorched above half their height, damage is minor," write Bickford and Newcomb (1947). *Mortality is ex cessive when more than four-fifths of the crown is scorched.*

Temporary reduction in rate of growth is noticeable on trees where needles are scorched between half and four-fifths their height. Of course there is no damage where a few trees are killed if others are left unharmed within six or eight feet.

To reduce costs and avoid uncontrolled fires, full use should be made of roads, streams, fields, and other barriers. Footpaths are enough, oftentimes, along which to set the fires.

The fires to condemn unanimously are unsupervised annual fires. *"Controlled" or "prescribed" fire is* NOT *used annually*—only at periods of three or more years when the brush begins to gets troublesome, or just before a dangerous amount of combustible material (grass, leaves, needles) accumulates.

Burning should be done only in the dormant season. This is November through February in the Deep South. Many hunting preserves are not burned until March, though this activity should have been completed by the early days of that month. Dry weather occasionally occurs in February. When your plans for burning encounter a dry season, the thing to do is to abandon your plans until the following year.

As I noted earlier, we can assure bobwhites plenty of winter foods—from mid-October to May—with bicolor lespedeza and no fire. We have demonstrated that fact reasonably well on Palachucola Club, Garnett, South Carolina, and Ed Wohlwender's land, adjoining Fort Benning, Columbus, Georgia. The bicolor seed remains easily available because it can be cultivated every second or third year, an operation which destroys the pine needles and tree leaves before they cover the seed too heavily. The same design of food strip planted to browntop millet and sesbania seemed similarly successful. In fact the latter combination is needed on soils which are too wet for bicolor.

I am afraid the unburned woods are nearly useless for summer range. The insect life appears scarce and hard to catch. Other foods are also scarce. Red bugs, mites, lice, and wood ticks may be intolerable to the birds in unburned woods through the summer months. We have not yet studied sufficiently the birds themselves which always give the trustworthy answers to such questions. So this is one of the jobs to be done yet. Don't quote me as saying quail will or will not raise in unburned woodland. I don't know.

As for hunting: A fully stocked forest of young trees is too rough for easy hunting. When trees reach 10- or 12-inch diameters, shooting is not bad. The dense stands may be the refuge system we want. Thinning with an axe and saw is a profitable enterprise. A stand of 8 to 10-inch trees too thick for hunting will yield a lot of pulpwood. The trees you leave will grow more rapidly, soon replacing the volume of wood removed. The spaces left will let you shoot. So you can have trees with no birds; or birds with only half enough trees; or a 98 percent stand of trees with birds.

If you will use fire carefully, I recommend it to you.

CHAPTER X
CROPLAND

To manage cropland to produce quail foods satisfactorily has proven very difficult and quite uncertain. Food in cropland is generally abundant for a few weeks in fall—then scarce or gone when needed most. Some years the cropland does a fair job of feeding the birds. Other years the same fields fail to do so. At best the proposition is complex and none too dependable.

Bobwhites increased with the advent of cultivated fields in the big eastern forests and the vast prairie areas during pioneer days. These greater numbers resulted from increased foods—weed seeds and waste grain. But then livestock increased, which accounts for much of the recent decline in food and numbers of bobwhite quail.

By accident, farming has left numerous coverts and considerable foods haphazardly about the farms. Occasionally the food and cover are close together around fields. Hedges along fence rows and ditches and property lines have provided chance cover. So has the brush in gullies, along creeks, and in natural drains. Roadsides once harbored numerous coveys. Weed seeds of the fields, waste grain from the crops, and wild foods on idle or abandoned fields fed the birds haphazardly here and there. Yet it seems nothing less than a miracle that bobwhites have survived in numbers where they depended on cropland. Actually, the brushy areas were unrecognized wildlife lands.

Most of the weeds of the fields have no value as food for quail. Hundreds of thousands of acres of cropland have nothing but cheat grass, sandspurs, cockle-burs, coffee-weed, dog-fennel, crab grass, Mexican clover (pursley), poor Joe (buttonweed), and lamb's quarter. These are no good as foods. Also, surprisingly, few of the clover seeds are eaten. Crimson clover, white clover, red clover, sweet clover, and alsike are not eaten by quail.

Patch farming, small fields surrounded by woodland, have supported many birds. This combination supplies food and cover in greater abundance (if ungrazed) than any other pattern of land use can do incidentally. Idle fields, with their annual weeds and new brush coverts, have supported many quail and much hunting. Only the thinly grown woods, annually burned, have rivalled the weedy fields and idle land in support of quail. None of these ways of land management, however, are permanent in American agriculture. They are on their way out, and have been during the steady decline of quail numbers.

Too many writers have deplored the advent of better farming because it reduced the foods and cover for quail. Bobwhites, it is true, disappeared as the careless farming was replaced, and as livestock consumed the last habitats. Since our agricultural welfare will not be turned backward in the name of wildlife conservation, a sound program for future management of bobwhites must be in harmony with modern landuse and the practices employed in its care. It must be a part of profitable agriculture.

In cropland, we must reckon again with wildlife-land. It was destruction of the natural cover on lands, once left unconsciously as wildlife land, that our writers have deplored. As cattle glean the fields foods disappear. Even the edges of fields are useless to bobwhites unless cover is near the food. The cropland supports no quail while it is freshly plowed. Neither does a winter field of wheat, or oats, or rye, or barley.

Edges of fields adjacent to most kinds of woodland produce little of crops or hay. The tree roots claim the greater portion of moisture and plant food. Annual plants cannot compete. Seldom well-covered with crop growth, these edges are subject to erosion and leeching. They are unsightly, and unused. Here lies the commonest opportunity to employ wildlife land—at the edge of cropland.

Dedicated to perennial vegetation of the right sort, field borders cease to be a problem in erosion (Davison 1941). A strip of bicolor lespedeza here offers the food we need for our bobwhites at that particular part of the farm. You can't feed your birds on "half a loaf", so don't make the mistake of planting a row or two of bicolor. That isn't enough. Make your food strip 12 to 15 feet wide—no more than 20 feet. Add an equal width of sericea where you need a turn-row between cropland and bicolor.

In the North the best quail food is said to be corn, as technicians (Fry 1938; Hawkins 1937; Allen 1938; Errington 1936, Gerstel 1942) seem to agree. Unless a perennial such as bicolor is discovered for the northern states, corn should be the choice of the game manager. Of course it must be grown on cropland which is suitable for corn production.

If winter feeding has any merit (and the authors listed in the paragraph above express grave doubts of its practical use), corn grown as a regular crop may be placed in shocks near the best cover. Such feeding should not, however, be an emergency measure. If you use it, put the food there early and see that the corn remains available every day through good weather as well as bad until late spring storms are no longer even a threat. (Massachusetts prohibits the leaving of corn in fields over winter, due to the corn borer. Whether this applies to corn shocks on borders for game birds, or whether the corn borer is actually controlled by such a law, is open to question.)

Grass borders, theoretically, should be used in western areas which fail to grow sericea. What to use for dependable quail-food on field borders in the west has not been determined, so far as I can learn.

We are not sure yet of other techniques designed to make cropland produce good populations of quail. The wildlife border, of course, is dependable and most economical. Contour hedges are recommended in bulletins for wildlife in general. But will they support quail? Not in single-row hedges, perhaps. Nor in two-row plantings. It is also probable that the hedge will have to contain an essential food to carry the birds through periods when the adjacent cropland is bare of food. So both food and cover are necessary in a successful hedge.

Small fields can be managed to produce winter-foods in the South. Florida beggarweed, once started, will volunteer in corn fields and supply large qualities of food and cover if grazing is not permitted. The range of this quail food is limited to the Gulf and South Atlantic areas. This annual cropland beggarweed is less palatable than bicolor, and is unnecessary where field borders or hedges of bicolor are grown around and across the fields. The chief weakness of Florida beggarweed is that birds are left without food by early spring plowing.

The annual lespedezas, common, Kobe, and Korean, are good quail foods. When grown in rotations, they *sometimes* provide food in abundance. Unless the rotation is in strips, leaving lespedeza every year in the same field, the lespedeza is not a dependable supply of food. Lespedeza which is grazed or cut for hay does not have sufficient seed left for the quail.

Cowpeas and soybeans grown in ungrazed croplands also feed quail; though rabbits, deer, and doves compete with them for food. Ordinary cowpeas and soybeans deteriorate in wet years. A few varieties of each have largely overcome this handicap. Soybeans may closely rival corn as a food for the northern states.

Though these cropland foods are abundant in fall and early winter, most of them are destroyed by plowing before the birds cease to need them in the spring.

Also, grazing of crop fields in fall and winter seriously reduces bobwhite food and cover, often below a livable condition. Unless wildlife land such as hedges, windbreaks, fence rows, gullies, and streambanks are allowed to grow cover, cropland will add little to quail populations beyond the field-border.

CHAPTER XI
PASTURES

Pasture land is perhaps the most difficult kind of land-use to combine with quail management. Though native pastures often support fair numbers of bobwhites, livestock compete severely with the birds. They eat almost every plant that would grow seed for the quail; and they remove most of the good ground cover of grass, honeysuckle, and native weeds.

The better improved pastures contribute almost nothing to bobwhites—no nesting cover, no winter food, no winter or summer shelter—only insects and green leaves in summertime. The intensity of grazing, the mowing to keep down weeds and brush, and the kind of vegetation grown make the improved pasture too barren for our birds. Nevertheless, recently developed techniques may make it possible to produce high populations of quail in pasture areas.

IMPROVED PASTURES

If quail are ever raised within well-developed pastures, it will be on wildlife lands protected from grazing and mowing. The Soil Conservation Service has developed a permanent living fence, for the purpose, using a single row of multiflora rose planted a foot or two apart (Steavenson 1946). This technique is quite new; and untried in much of the quail range. By 1948 it had proven beyond question to be a fence of peculiar beauty, service, and dependability.

The rose fence grows about eight feet high and eight feet wide. It makes a stockproof fence in three, four, or five years, depending on the soils and the care given it the first year. It promises to be the American living-fence of the future. Hundreds of miles of this new fence were established on farms in Missouri, Illinois, and states to the eastward between 1940 and 1948. For farm game, particularly quail, the original design (a single-row fence) needs revision. Both cover and food are insufficient for winter.

Any rose is an extremely poor food for bobwhites. We must consider it negligible. A single-row fence of multiflora rose has no ground cover of grass beneath—a lack of which means no nesting cover in summer, no protective warmth in winter. Therefore, an area of wildlife land containing both a first-class bird-food and ground cover must be protected by the rose. Designs to meet these essential needs are simple, and will not take large areas of land.

I do not want to predict the exact shape of the bird coverts which may someday produce game birds around and across the best improved pastures; but you'll be interested to know the designs already being established. Instead of a single fence (8 feet wide), we are testing double fences, separated by as little as 6 feet and as much as 17 feet. High-quality foods such as bicolor lespedeza are planted in the space between. Of course small areas of grass are left for ground cover, too.

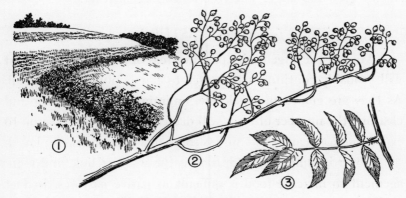

MULTIFLORA ROSE
(1) Contour rose fence; (2) fruited branch; (3) leaves.

Another design is to surround small steep areas of gullies—which never make good pasture anyway—with the rose fence; then you put bird-food inside. This separates the land best suited for birds from land most profitable as pasture. This design was never very successful when we had to use wire and posts. Short lines of wire fence are difficult to keep tight; a wire fence on the contour is almost impossible to build and keep up. The living fence of multiflora rose is far more successful.

In the same manner farm ponds are fenced against livestock in the Midwest, leaving room inside the fence for good quail-food plants, protected against grazing. The opportunities to produce quail in pasture areas have not been exhausted, you see.

Until these practices are measured more definitely, they are only promises. We need that living fence very much. Farmers and agricultural leaders object to and are removing the osage orange hedges which once supported hundreds of coveys in the prairie country. The osage hedge sapped too much land on either side; it grew too large. The rose fence does neither.

NATIVE PASTURE

Most of the large native pasture areas of the South and West will probably continue with scarce to fair populations of quail. As they are grazed more closely, or improved by mowing and clearing, the number of birds will decrease. There is no reason to expect increases anywhere unless some new practice is employed.

Cover is none too good; food is the weakest link; and management to increase food is difficult in native pastures. In fact no improvement of food and cover has been demonstrated widely, if at all, in such areas. Perhaps the same techniques now being developed to make "improved" pastures habitable for quail will be useful in "native" pastures too.

The palmetto pastures of Florida and the Gulf Coast provide reasonably good cover. Wax myrtle is a good cover plant, and one of the foods eaten by the birds. It can be protected. Simply don't grub it out or mow it down where you want bobwhites.

In the Gulf Coast climate, quail seem to need less proteins and fats in their foods. The cold is less severe. Tender, green leaves are available the year 'round. The birds are slightly smaller. Insects, too, are available more months of the year. Grass seeds

ripen almost every month. Quail may live easier than in the
colder climates, but they do not grow in any greater abundance.

In Florida the coveys live at the edge of grassy sloughs,
with native cover along the edge. The drier uplands are almost
devoid of food—and birds. At present our best means to manage
these pasture lands for the most food is to burn about half of
each in alternate years. This increases foods such as nut-grasses,
insects, and—on some soils—partridge peas.

In western Oklahoma, as I have explained elsewhere, our
sandy native pastures fed quail well in summer with abundant
insect life. The oak brush gave sufficient cover, then. But winter
foods were scarce, and the birds moved out to the croplands and
into the brushy cover of creeks to spend the winter. They
migrated back to the pastures in the spring. Wintering livestock,
however, ate up most of the winter foods and cover, even in the
fields and along the streams. Populations per 100 acres of pasture
are, therefore, discouragingly low.

What to do in native pastures to measurably increase quail
is still partly to be found. As I have suggested, a living fence
would be a blessing; an opportunity to protect an acre or two
(or several) where a food plant could be grown. In such areas,
however, food competition from rabbits, field rats, and other
birds will be severe, perhaps prohibitive.

THE VALUE OF FIRE IN NATIVE PASTURES

Native pastures will at times need burning to keep them in
good condition for both grazing livestock and bobwhites. This
need arises when livestock fail to consume the grass of a previous season.

In western Oklahoma I found in the early 1930's that quail

in summer avoid areas of old grass—in heavy stands of two or three years' growth. They would not nest or rear their young in such cover. I attributed it to two things: poor feeding conditions and excessive heat. Insects are harder to catch in old stemmy grass. Both seeds and insects are hidden in such cover. The added heat in old dead stems is very noticeable, as compared to green stems alone where transpiration is greater and breezes can move about. I then concluded that either grazing or burning was necessary to keep summer range in good condition for birds. We burned wherever light grazing of the previous year left a high percentage of old grass. I still think those conclusions are right. They apply as much or more to Florida and all the South.

CHAPTER XII
IDLE LAND

As I pointed out elsewhere, bobwhites thrive generally with the cover and food that grows in early stages of idle land. An abandoned field usually produces food in adequate quantity for two or three years; foods such as sunflowers and ragweeds in the western areas; lespedeza, ragweeds, bullgrass, and beggarweeds in the South; barnyard grass, foxtail, and ragweed in the North. Briars and protective grasses begin to cover the idle fields. In spite of these beneficial conditions, idle land is an extremely poor way to produce bobwhites.

Idle land is expensive to the landowners. Most idle land is left that way because it has become too poor to produce a profitable crop. It is a symbol of waste; a testament of abuse; a glaring example of poor management. Idle land contributes nothing to farm income. Its future is a hopeless blank as a land resource, until a better land use is planned and established. Those old fields which grow up to cockle-burs, sandspurs, cheat grass, Mexican clover, and such plants are useless even to quail since they will not eat the seeds.

The idle land in the quail range, 1945, totalled approximately 17 million acres. This is a conservative estimate, supplied by the Soil Conservation Service, from agricultural statistics and surveys. Seventeen million acres is a lot of land, and the acreage was actually much greater. It is 2 percent of the land in the quail range. Field borders, open areas in woodlands, and countless odd areas in fields and pastureland, were also idle but unrecognized. Still some people say, "We cannot find room for wildlife land on American farms."

Idle land has no place in good farm economy. It is not a land use. It does not fit into any program of soil conservation. It should not be recommended, though numerous writers have advocated it as a wildlife management practice. Farmers cannot afford idle land. Happily, bobwhites can be produced in greater numbers and at less cost without idle land.

BROOMSEDGE

Idle fields generally turn to broomsedge after a few years. Stoddard pointed out the unfavorable factors related to broomsedge, the old field grass of the South. Cottonrats became so numerous as to be detrimental to quail, destroying nests. Bobwhites will not use the oldest sedge fields: food is scarce and unavailable in waist-high broomsedge and other grasses which accumulate heavily unless burned. Many people burn their broomsedge fields to benefit quail. This treatment is a temporary one, and is therefore at fault. Broomsedge should be replaced by a better land use. Its control by fire alone is an endless and annual task which makes no progress until you proceed with a more definite land use.

Keep fire out of broomsedge until trees have seeded in and grown to a height of 15 or 20 feet, thus shading the grasses, if the land use is to be woodland. Or if it is to be pasture, fertilize, lime and seed as you do to develop good grazing. Or for cropland (if suitable) follow the correct practices advocated for that particular soil.

If you plan to change the idle broomsedge field to wildlife land, plant strips of a good food and manage the remainder as woodland or cropland as you choose. A rule to remember is: it is never profitable to manage more than 5 (possibly 10) percent of a field for quail. You can produce all the food the birds can eat on this small portion of the land. In woodland you can do the same thing on about 1 percent of the land. So manage the remaining 95 to 99 percent of the land for some other profitable use. This gives you a sound land-use economy; and keeps your efforts for bobwhites within reasonable expenditures. Thus you plan idle, broomsedge land for usefulness. (See wildlife land, cropland, woodland, or pasture land.)

NAIL DOWN THE TOPSOIL

SOIL CONSERVATION DISTRICTS

In the foregoing chapters we have shown how land management practices influence bobwhites. The revolutionary simplicity of those practices will not have escaped those who have tried the older, more complex recommendations for bobwhite management. Those whose earlier efforts have been less successful may have caught a spirit of new hope, a promise of attainment toward the goal of the quail enthusiast. Nevertheless, we should not expect general application of these simple practices on the land, guided by books alone. Education will play its usual, subordinate role. Widespread success will come only as a part of a well organized program of action.

The heartening developments of bicolor lespedeza and multiflora rose were part of a much more important scheme of human endeavor—a land management program to make better use of American soils, a determination to conserve the land itself against erosion, waste, and misuse. The activities of soil conservation districts are dedicated to maintaining and improving good land for people. Bobwhite production is one of those things that many people want.

Farmers and ranchers like bobwhites. Most of them want more on their own lands. Many landowners in every county are ready and anxious to provide sufficient food and cover for them. They only await neighborhood proof that a certain practice or a particular food is worth inclusion in their land management. The district organization serves every community. Of course, some may be depending even yet on our laws or pen raised birds, or the hunters to provide bobwhite abundance by some magic formula. Or they may live in forlorn hope that "nature will provide." But plenty of landowners are willing to manage their lands for more birds.

Since bobwhite management is a part of the owner's business, a plan for the birds can hardly be made without making a permanent plan at the same time for all the farm, including cropland, woodland, pastures, hayland, etc. Wildlife land must be intermingled judiciously with these other land uses if you expect satisfactory returns from your efforts. Bobwhites have no security until you have adopted such a stabilized pattern of land use.

The soil conservation approach to agricultural endeavor embodies three definite aids which are no less essential to wildlife objectives than they are to production of domestic livestock, cash crops, and timber:

1. An understanding of the land, its soils, and their economic uses.

2. A land-use layout designating the location of pastures, crops, timber, and wildlife land.

3. A plan of operation including the application of soil and water conservation practices on the land, and provision for their continued care as needed.

These are the charts and the blueprints that go into a plan of land management. They have been adopted by soil conservation districts as the farm plan to guide landowners. Into such plans go the features which will influence abundance of bobwhites downward, upward, or without change, as the landowner applies the practices to his soils.

With soil conservation you can support quail better than nature or man has been able to do before. This is true only in cases where bobwhite management has been considered, found acceptable, and has been applied. The welfare of bobwhites is an elective you may choose or refuse. It is possible to have complete and adequate soil conservation on thousands of farms with no homes provided for quail. At the other extreme you can have more quail with complete soil conservation than you can have without it. You will have to choose. Neither a soil conservation technician nor a game conservation technician can decide for you. Theirs are only suggestions.

Thus you will see that management for the bobwhite will not be universal. It will not be spontaneous. It will depend on the owner and the tenants of farm lands and ranch lands, but their interest can be encouraged by others.

SOIL CONSERVATION DISTRICTS

During several decades past, we have had organized clubs of sportsmen; but their efforts seldom dealt with production through land management. A few farmer-sportsmen clubs have been organized at one time or another for the single purpose of game management, usually designed to ration the hunting to authorized hunters. To attack the restoration problem on a state-wide scale demands more than either of these organizations formerly had to offer. The newly organized soil conservation district is the most promising agency to perform the task.

To assure efficiency and success of land management, technical assistance for every farm is usually needed to determine a sound plan. The assignment of soil conservation technicians to these districts give landowners that part of the aid required. The districts are also empowered to seek and accept assistance from any agency and individual who will offer a contribution to soil conservation and good use of land. State game departments, game clubs, and the Fish and Wildlife Service can help as we shall see.

In a brief 8 years—beginning with Arkansas, North Carolina, South Carolina and Georgia in 1937—every state in the United States passed a law enabling farmers to create soil conservation districts. Alabama, in the southern heart of the bobwhite range, was the first to organize the entire state, embracing 231 thousand farms—32 million acres of land. South Carolina completed its organization next with 137 thousand farms—19 million acres. With the lagging exception of Missouri, Tennessee and Pennsylvania, the range of the bobwhite quail rapidly became a part of one of these new soil conservation districts. There were nearly 1,500 organized districts in the bobwhite range by early 1949.

Thus the four and a half million unwieldy number of farms were divided into smaller organized compartments—as few as 3 districts each for little Rhode Island and Delaware, as many as

77 in Oklahoma, 91 in Iowa, and 148 in Texas. Alabama had completed its organizational job with 12 large districts; South Carolina with 21 which were later subdivided still further. Big or little, the districts went to work. Almost without exception they stated as one of their objectives "the conservation of game and fish and other wildlife resources."

In 1938 the districts within the quail range had less than 50 technical men assigned to guide cooperating farmers. Even had we known the techniques, these few could have influenced land management for quail but little. This meager group of agricultural land workers, however, grew to about 8,000 in the quail range by 1949. Thus direct assistance to every farmer was no longer an impossibility. If agricultural assistance is continued for these district organizations, quail restoration will become a common accomplishment. There will be no need for a "wildlife extension specialist" in every county. Money can be spent better with districts.

The governing boards of districts have shown their willingness to set standards for every sound conservation practice for the land. As contemplated by their legislatures, the governing boards sought assistance from every agency, public or private, who would contribute to their planning—either ideas, materials, or machinery—anything required to get land management in practice.

Nothing was more difficult, however, than for the district governing boards themselves to realize the opportunities and responsibilities before them. Progress was slow but steady. There were those in conservation circles who despaired of the huge task while it remained an awkwardly growing juvenile.

South Carolina took the lead in the next step to strengthen

the functioning of districts. The 21 boards of supervisors organized themselves into a state association. The late E. C. McArthur, Gaffney, was their first president and chief organizer. He believed that the difficulties in his own district must be facing the farmers in other districts too. He didn't know how to solve many of their problems but he believed they could find solutions together. He demanded recognition of the district organization as a coalition of farmers—not a rubber stamp for some government institution. The districts needed the help of all agencies that had a stake in the returns from agriculture.

Mr. McArthur was not concerned primarily with game conservation. It was one of the lesser objectives, yet it was a real one. He and his colleagues wanted the land conserved. They wanted the land used wisely and profitably, but without deterioration. If game conservation, fish production and any other use of land contributed to the welfare of the land and the people who owned it, the directors of the soil conservation districts were for it.

Since then many states have organized statewide associations of district governing boards. They are a powerful group of forward looking men. Natural evolution combined the state associations into a national organization in 1946. The soil conservation districts have attained stability and self-respect.

STATE GAME DEPARTMENTS CAN AID

Meanwhile it was becoming apparent to a few hunters and game management technicians that farmers and ranchers almost alone had the power to provide bobwhites in greater abundance, or to allow them to shift for themselves as usual in their world of uncertainty and insufficiencies.

The first game departments to accord formal recognition to the soil conservation district as a potential factor in quail management were Georgia, Virginia and Mississippi, back in 1940 and '41. These three pioneering game departments offered gifts of sericea lespedeza seed to farmers to help them establish wildlife borders—then a new practice of land management. Wildlife borders became the first recognized "wildlife-land" of agriculture. Though sericea proved to be a very poor food—and food we needed—it held the outpost until the top-food, bicolor lespedeza, was developed as its companion or successor. Other states began to help the new districts in succeeding years. This cooperation in land management was a new advancement for both game and agricultural interests. It began to work.

Following the examples set by Georgia, Virginia, and Mississippi, the state game departments in Alabama, Arkansas, Kentucky, Illinois, Louisiana, Maryland, North Carolina and West Virginia (perhaps others) began to see the soil conservation approach as an opportunity. They worked out cooperative arrangements with the districts, usually supplying seeds for border plantings and furthering the idea educationally. After the discovery and testing of bicolor food strips in woodland, first one and then another game department sponsored that type of planting, also. Illinois, Kentucky and other states broadened their assistance, supplying multiflora rose, evergreens, and other things they believed would help produce game.

In most of these state projects, the Fish and Wildlife Service participated by supplying 75 percent of the state's funds through a Federal Act, generally known as the Pittman-Robertson Act. Until mid-1947 the amount of such funds to aid soil conservation district activities was still very meager, compared to other activities and the needs of bobwhite hunters. In 1947 Congress increased this annual Federal Aid fund about four-fold. The quail hunter may fervently hope that all of this increased money is not spent on large land purchases, general surveys, and other unproductive projects.

State game department aid in quail management will necessarily be limited by finances, personnel, and policy. The following opportunities, however, are sound and encouraging:

1. They can supply enough seed and other planting materials to help establish 100 or more demonstrations of each good practice per county. The number should be sufficient to demonstrate the value of each practice in every community. The contributions should be available over a period of 5 or 10 years, rather than 1 or 2.

2. They should study, observe and refine each practice. This work to date has had to be done largely by technicians of the Soil Conservation Service. A number of state game technicians began to progress through this stage of self-training in the 1940's.

3. They might train every game warden by experience so they in turn can teach hunters and landowners about the need of land management, the practices which successfully produce quail, and the ways they can help individually. Unsuccessful practice must be discouraged!

GAME CLUBS

Game clubs can help encourage landowners in quail restoration. An example will illustrate a method.

In the summer of 1946, the Hinds County Sportsmen Club,

Jackson, Mississippi, reorganized—as local game clubs have often done. They wanted to do something to produce more game—along with their fellowship banquets, and lobbying for better laws and regulations. Frankly, they didn't know what to do, and they admitted it.

One of the district commissioners and a soil conservation technician attended their meeting and saw a potentially powerful ally. They suggested land management—food and cover plantings—which were already contemplated by the district.

The club wanted to be specific. "What do you recommend? What do you plant? How can we help?" they asked.

They had never seen bicolor lespedeza. In the absence of such knowledge they had thought of the old practices: cowpeas, annual lespedezas, sorghums, etc. on cropland. Naturally they were not very hopeful since those older plantings were no longer popular or very helpful.

In short, this is what they decided to do:

First, they put every member who owned land on a Land Management Committee. Second, they asked those owners to test—on their own land—the new bicolor in the latest patterns of land use—borders, woodland strips, and hedges. Third, they agreed to help get enough plants and seeds for further plantings if the first trials proved successful. The club properly reserved judgment and withheld endorsement pending demonstrated results of more quail on the managed lands of its pioneering members. The soil conservation technicians made district plans, furnished bicolor seed and plants, and showed the landowning sportsmen how and where to plant.

Neighboring counties learned of the field test operations being sponsored by the landowning members of the Hinds

County Club. They offered financial assistance and the lands of their leading sportsmen to try the same practices. These offers were made to the soil conservation district governing board, and were accepted. The districts were encouraged to sponsor the improvement of wildlife-land through the common interest of landowning sportsmen. Both local and national assistance thus became available.

This approach saves sportsmen's clubs the waste of large sums on useless projects. It assures understanding. It saves embarrassment and loss of time which follow unsound activities. We all like to experiment—to learn by trial, rather than to accept an idea ready made. Game clubs are no exception.

The obvious results are to encourage every hunter who owns land to treat it with successful practices. They naturally encourage their friends to do likewise. No one will know the value of land management for bobwhite restoration any better than the landowning hunter. The sportsmen, too, will recognize the farm conservation plan, sponsored by the soil conservation district as the once-missing route to game production.

In this way, hunters are providing for themselves. No longer are they foolish enough to wait for "George to do it." George won't do it. He won't grow quail for unknown hunters. It is really pathetic to hear a landowning sportsman complaining that "the game department or someone ought to do something to bring back an abundance of bobwhites."

One caution seems necessary to hunting clubs and game departments. Their first thoughts usually run to "restrictions" or "privileges." Game departments want some assurance that the farmer will take care of the birds and keep the land managed correctly. They often ask farmers to close their lands against all hunting for from 2 to 5 years; also demand a right to trap "surplus birds" for restocking elsewhere. Sometimes they insist that a farmer who obtains state assistance must not post his land . against hunting. *No farmer should accept aid if he has to agree to such restrictions, or give special privileges!*

In the first place, any farmer who will voluntarily manage some of his land—furnish labor and machinery to prepare it, and the effort to seed or plant a permanent food strip—that man is equally or more a conservationist than those who would ask some quarantee. A man who plants for bobwhites has no intention of destroying them.

In the second place, he won't have any surplus birds to transplant. Transplanting isn't worth the effort it takes. The "surplus" birds should be left to hunt, by the farmer and any friend he chooses. He should not be required to permit hunting, nor to prevent it, if he prefers otherwise.

Bobwhite management does not need to encompass management of the landowner, too. Unfortunately, there are people who would dictate the terms of conservation so as to exclude the landowner from the fruits of his own endeavors. Bobwhites will never be produced—farmers will not be encouraged—by such tactics.

And finally, if game technicians, educators, and administrators will admit the pitiful meagerness of bobwhite populations as they are, the need of intelligent land management will be obvious as a means to overcome our sublime omission of this fundamental requirement.

CHAPTER XIV
BOBWHITE NUMBERS AND HUNTING

The man who manages his land to benefit bobwhites will have done the major job of production. In addition he will want to conserve—to hunt sensibly to avoid depletion by overhunting. Laws are unable to protect the birds, or to guide the bobwhite manager. He only needs to know a few simple principles about quail populations and when to stop hunting the coveys.

No one can manage well unless he has a fair knowledge of the numbers of birds upon his land. I don't mean a technical census. I refer to the size of coveys, the remainder to be left in each, and the natural expectation of their subsequent reproduction. Everyone also wants to know how many birds he may reasonably expect by management.

There is much misunderstanding about quail populations. Many people exaggerate their numbers.

As examples: One of my friends writes of "big coveys, 25 or 30 birds in each"; though the average is between 12 and 15 per covey. Another still believes a pair will raise two sets of young in one year; but this is the sheerest kind of unfounded optimism which *never* happens in the wild. No few hunters are surprised to learn that more than half of the pairs each year fail completely in their efforts to raise young. These are shocking revelations to many of our bobwhite fans. Nevertheless, coveys of only 12 to 15 birds, just one covey of young per pair each year, and complete failure of more than half the pairs is the commonplace expectancy for every part of the quail range. Greater optimism is foolish.

Leopold (1933) pointed to an area in Illinois, Missouri, southeastern Iowa, and parts of Indiana as probably the highest producing area in the bobwhite range. The Iowa state bulletin on its wildlife resources (1943) said the bobwhite is seen in largest numbers in several southeast counties, with a bird population as high as one bird to one acre. These word-pictures reflect an optimistic viewpoint far beyond the cold facts.

The Iowa bulletin estimated the state breeding stock of quail at 480,000 birds in the spring of 1943. This was only one pair of birds for each of Iowa's 209,000 farms which averaged 165 acres in size. According to their further estimates, bobwhites in Iowa nearly tripled in number by fall of the same year. Nevertheless 1,400,000 birds were no more than ½ covey per farm; it was a bird for each 25 acres. This figure is far short of one bird per acre. If it is a bitter disappointment—much less pleasant to write (and read)—yet it reflects the actual situation. If such startling low figures are shocking, they should also bring to mind that great opportunities must exist to substantially increase the meager population of birds. No one would try to increase a bird-per-acre population; but obviously a bird-per-25-acres needs attention. Our technicians and educators will gain much by substituting careful analyses for rosy phrases.

The Iowa figures might well be stated in still another way. Approximately 120,000 birds were harvested in the southern and east-central counties in 1942. This could hardly be more than 2 birds per farm, even in that good part of the state range. This amount of shooting cannot be very satisfactory. The pitiful part of the story is that the bulletin says, "Ordinarily, waste grain of the fields and weed seeds of the pastures and grain fields supply sufficient food."

Southeastern preserves yield an average kill of about 10 birds per 100 acres. Expressed another way, good quail land is that upon which 15 to 20 coveys can be found in 6 hours when hunted with good dogs. A hunting party usually covers about a thousand acres a day. These "good" lands support only 1 bird to 5 acres, one or two coveys per hundred acres.

According to Daniel W. Lay (1940) a population of slightly under 2 coveys per hundred acres of eastern Texas woodland was optimum with the best management then known. This is the same as in the Southeast.

For a farm or game preserve a covey on each 40 acres is generally considered very good hunting. At a figure of 13 or 14 birds in the average covey (most people use the number 15 which is a little high) this is 3 acres per bird. You may prefer to say a good population is 2 or 3 coveys per hundred acres. This population may be considered the best that has been obtained in any of the bobwhite range.

By the recently developed practices of land management we have produced 4 or 5 coveys by managing just one acre primarily for the birds. Good care of one acre will produce winter food for 50 or 60 birds which can be concentrated on 100 acres of land managed as woodland or cropland or both. This is more than double the population you can expect from managing 100 acres of cropland or woodland without setting aside small parcels of land to be managed primarily for quail. Considerable effort is now being employed to determine the practical possibilities of producing 100 birds on 100 acres of land by producing food on 2 or 3 acres out of each hundred; but only time and continued hard work will answer this hopeful endeavor one way or the other.

Just where the limit is beyond which quail populations can be pushed no higher is of course important. We are forced to accept the one-bird-per-acre limitation or less, since we have not been able to equal it. Meanwhile our efforts in management have plenty of room for application on the areas where no birds exist; also, where less than 4 or 5 coveys per hundred acres are now being supported. Even this goal is only halfway to the one-bird-per-acre ceiling. To attain the halfway goal will mean doubling the present population. With the simpler, more successful land management described herein, perhaps 4 coveys per hundred acres will be the rule rather than the exception, as now.

One belief which may be holding conservation back is the idea that you cannot accomplish much until the whole community or the whole state does something or other. You can have bobwhites on your own land, or have none, regardless of what your neighbors do on theirs. This implies, of course, that your management plan provides the essentials of a year-round home for bobwhites, all within your own boundaries. You can do this on the average farm.

We use the excuse too often that we can't do anything for our birds unless our neighbors go into a cooperative scheme with us. Many plans have been tried to make community areas produce more game and better hunting. But such an area requires almost impossible coordination of many human interests. The trials have largely failed. Individual action avoids most of these inherent difficulties.

Now don't exaggerate the benefits your neighbor might receive as a result of your conservation efforts. You won't make his hunting much better. Certainly some of your birds may cross over the line on occasion. Your neighbor may shoot them, too. But remember that the birds go over of their own free will, mostly because the other fellow has better food, or better cover. Birds will leave your land if you do not have enough.

Be a good neighbor; and above all, don't work up a mental sweat. Look to your land management. Make your place as attractive as you can. You'll always have birds.

In developing your entire farm to best advantage, you may find excellent cover across the line on your neighbor's land. You may have no place for cover on that part of your farm. It would look as though you have two choices: (1) leave that part of your land unimproved, or (2) develop it with your neighbor. You might declare a truce and keep that covey range an inviolate refuge for both, an undisturbed place for breeding stock in the wild. Neither of you would hunt that covey.

Or you might shoot the covey only when you two were together—gentlemen's agreement.

Or you could lease his cover for shooting rights.

Or you could take turns, year about, in hunting. Maybe you can figure a better way to make it worth while to develop the outer boundaries of your land as well as the middle of your properties.

There is, of course, a limit to the number of birds your land will support, even with all the food they can eat. When you have provided good food and cover by managing the land, your chief concern is to maintain the conditions as uniformly as possible year after year. Then you will need to hunt judiciously.

CAUTION IN HARVESTING THE BIRDS

Next year's broodstock depends upon the care exercised by the landowner and his hunting friends. Stop shooting when you have harvested about half your birds (fall population). Thus to replenish your full numbers each summer, you should leave 6 or 7 birds alive in each covey at the end of the shooting season. Or to say it another way, for every 6 or 7 birds left then, you can expect a covey of 12 to 15 birds at the opening of the next hunting season.

As a general rule you can be sure that quail have been heavily overshot and are very scarce on every acre of land where hunters are free to go without the landowners' permission. Even strict observation of closed seasons and state bag limits give virtually no protection to such areas; each covey is hunted by too many gunners who may unknowingly leave insufficient brood stock.

Particular care must be exercised to avoid overshooting on lands which are as open as most native pastures. Only in heavy cover such as swamps and thorny thickets can the birds escape the hunter who is careless or greedy or lacks understanding.

Stoddard and Komarek (1941 a), said: "Experience has shown that, for best results, coveys should not be moved by dog and gun more than once a week."

Most hunters like to shoot singles after they scatter from the covey rise. Others, however, suggest: "If you can produce enough birds so I can flush 15 coveys in a day, a hunting partner and I can take 20 birds on the covey rises. I wouldn't hunt the singles—wouldn't disturb them any more that day. I like to see plenty of coveys."

However you want to hunt, leave enough for the spring broodstock. The old idea of "leave 5 or 6 birds" is not caution enough—you'd better leave 6 or 7.

CHAPTER XV
THE THINGS TO DO, IN QUICK REVIEW

This brief chapter lists the essential things to do to have more bobwhites. It is a summary reminder, without details.

Our concept of "conservation" must be expanded to include "high production" as the basic method of meeting the demand for more farm-game.

To increase bobwhites, we must establish and maintain suitable habitat on the land. That means private land—in four-and-a-half million separate ownerships. Happily, each individual owner can have birds without waiting for his neighbors to act.

Adequate food and cover must be grown at each location on

a farm where a covey is wanted. One good winter food, plus grass and shrubby cover, will support the birds.

The most dependable quail habitat is provided by wildlife-land, managed simply for the essential food and cover plants adaptable to your particular location within the quail range.

For detailed suggestions on management techniques for "wildlife land", "woodland", "cropland", "pastures", and "idle land"—see each of those chapters. For on-the-farm assistance, in planning what to do and where and when to do it, ask the help of your local Soil Conservation Service technician. He will know the latest tricks in land management.

Avoid overshooting by leaving 6 or 7 birds per covey every year. Only the landowner (or exceptionally heavy cover) can prevent overharvesting of the birds.

To obtain farm-game production on groups of farms (or individual holdings) lend your aid to the soil conservation district where you hunt or own land.

Finally, recognize the landowner as the custodian and producer of our bobwhites. Encourage the landowner by more favorable laws, as suggested in the next and final chapter.

CHAPTER XVI
LAWS TO ENCOURAGE PRODUCTION

Though it is becoming evident that the landowners will make or destroy quail hunting, we may expect strong objections to favoring the landowners by slight changes of traditional laws. The following proposals are not revolutionary. They are progressive necessities to improve our hunting in the latter half of the twentieth century. Let us recall recent statements by some outstanding leaders.

Judge George W. Wood (1939) told the Fourth North American Wildlife Conference, "The general rule in the United States is that every person to whom the state has issued a hunting license may hunt and take game in every place where he has a right to be, provided he does not infringe upon or injure the rights of others.

"This last clause touches the very essence of the difficulties which arise between the sportsman and the landowner . . . that is to me the most dangerous in our present system. Every hunter seems to think that because he holds a license he has a right to go onto anyone's land and take game. I think that if we were going to get any place we must educate the hunter to the fact that he has no right on the landowner's place without the consent of the landowner himself."

Why not change the law slightly? Provide that a license is null and void until the hunter HAS the consent of the landowner.

At the same conference (1939) Leopold asserted, "We will have no conservation worthy of the name until food and cover for wildlife is deliberately instead of accidentally provided for." From his surveys he found that "not more than one farm in every five is capable of wintering any game bird" in the cornbelt.

He recalled the 1930 Game Policy of the American Game Association. Item 2 read: "Recognize the landowner as the custodian of public game on all (non-public) land."

Of progress toward that goal Leopold said, "This idea was the heart and pith of all the 1930 policy, but I fear it is still largely a hope rather than a reality. The 1930 policy not only recognized the farmer's right to post; it urged him to use that right. It urged him not to stop posting, but to go farther and control the shooting and to improve the food and the cover. Most states today recognize the farmer's right to post, but they urge him NOT to use it."

American sportsmen demand freedom to hunt; and many

have hoped for free hunting. The present generation and the future ones cannot depend on these free blessings in any abundance. Your license dollars are not enough to buy birds, land management, or hunting privileges. It is time to reconsider this so-called God-given right to hunt the wildlife of our country.

Certainly the ownership of bobwhites and squirrels and rabbits is lawfully vested in the state; that of migratory birds such as waterfowl and doves in the national government's cooperation with Canada and Mexico. Because wildlife (except fish in farm-ponds) are free to move from farm to farm, we are not likely to change our interpretation of these laws of ownership. I would not suggest it. It is timely, however, for every hunter and every landowner to revise his attitude toward his own rights, his responsibilities, and his opportunities to pursue farm-game species. This is particularly true regarding our favorite—the bobwhite.

Let's not stop with answering "Whose bird is he?" by giving the legal answer "Everybody's". The laws generally recognize the right of the landowner to say who shall hunt the birds as long as they are on his land; also that he may prevent any and all people from shooting at any time. Sounds good, but farmers can't stay home all the time to guard the birds. Besides, it puts the burden of law enforcement on the landowner.

Landowners would like to believe and say "The birds are mine as long as they are on my place." They'd like for the hunters to admit it. Farmers, like merchants and laborers, will do a better job with things belonging to them. Things left only in their custody are never as dear, and often become an aggravation. Birds are like that. Farm and ranch owners see no incentive to keep "everybody's birds" in their custody throughout the year, until some hunter wants to come after them in the open shooting season. The difference between state ownership and individual ownership is separated by a very narrow line of demarcation. Maybe we can avoid this stiff barrier by a new kind of consideration.

A concession to the farmers will obtain compensations of greater value to the hunters. If the laws or regulations of the state required a hunter to have permission from the landowner, farmers would have the kind of protection they need. The law should state specifically that the hunting license is null and void, unless accompanied by the landowner's permission. Federal permits, both scientific permits and duck stamps, are contingent upon permission granted by the local authority—the state. In other words the state would only issue a hunting right insofar as its equity goes—including hunting rights to any land owned or leased by the state, but not private lands. The permit from the landowner should be a written one though oral permission might suffice in the absence of prosecution by the owner.

Revolutionary? No!

Virginia enacted a similar law in 1946. Some states imply these limitations in their trespass laws. For example, you need the owner's permission in some states when you hunt on land with a fence around it (this indicating human occupation). In numerous states the landowners' right to post their properties is a partial answer to the problem. Nevertheless, the state game administration and the prowling hunter will find a none-too-friendly feeling among landowners until the state sells its hunting licenses subject to the will of the landowner. It's a fair proposition to both.

The old idea was not so bad when game was present by the

will-of-God, and not by the management of the landowner. Hunters have believed commonly that "Nature will take care of our game, if given a chance." There's no need to change the laws if we wish to continue our dependence on nature and chance. Our theme is management of the land, to have better food, more shelter; and thus more birds which may then be shot in sport. And only the landowner can do this management. For selfish reasons alone sportsmen need to encourage landowners in every way possible to manage their land, to produce something to shoot!

Now, it's a well known fact that when people give purposeful care to something, they seldom allow its abuse. The landowner is the man who can prevent overshooting better than any limit on bag or season. I am not suggesting a change in these laws; but desire to point out a natural law which supplements them. The daily bag limit by law is a rationing system, and a maximum believed to be sufficient for any but a glutton. It is also supposed to have something to do with assuring the next year's breeding stock; which, however, it does not and cannot do.

We must look to the farm owner to "regulate" the stopping point each year. He needs assurance that his is the responsibility of full custodianship; his birds to raise and feed; his privilege to govern in the harvest. A lot of paper has been used to discuss "farmer-sportsman relationship." Well, the real feat is to work out the producer-consumer problem.

Farmer-sportsman relationship is a misnomer, anyhow. Many of the biggest hunters are landowners. Their problem is simply to produce hunting for themselves. They represent both the farmer and the sportsman. Many farmers harvest their own surplus game, quite often with some friend from town.

It won't suit every hunter who has a gun, but here's a suggestion to those who want quail hunting: Better select a piece of land where you can obtain hunting privileges by buying, leasing, or doing a favor for the owner. The only places worth hunting will be the ones where the intelligent owner puts out effort (and some expense) to have more bobwhites than haphazard farming is going to produce. This is not a new system or a new idea. The best hunting in the quail range today is there by the owner's intent and work—not because the game laws have been such and such. Hundreds of thousands of farms, on the other hand, provide poor hunting, and often none at all, because the conservation there is nothing more than protection by law and sportsmen's creeds.

To support my theme further, some additional excerpts from the North American Wildlife Conference held in Detroit in 1939 are pertinent.

Said Aldo Leopold (1939): "Any system which does not leave to the individual farmer the control of his land of *who hunts* and *how much,* cannot be called any general answer to the farmer-sportsman problem in the United States. Unless and until the individual farmer chooses his own hunters and specifies how many birds they may kill, the system isn't safe enough for quail. Pheasants can stand it but not quail."

Albert M. Day, who later became Chief of the Fish and Wildlife Service, stated, following the formal papers: "I have listened with a great deal of interest to the discussions of farmer-sportsman relationships. We all agree that this is one of the most vexing problems in the vast area from the Rocky Mountains eastward to the Atlantic. . . . We can never hope to have enough lands set aside as hunting grounds, either state or federal, to meet the needs of our times. It would be unjustifiable from an economic standpoint. . . . Wildlife must continue to be reared in large measure on private lands, and our concern must be the means of encouraging such production."

The lesson plainly points to the landowner, millions of them, as the key figure in bobwhite conservation. It is no exaggeration to say that restoration of the bobwhite quail is an agricultural pursuit—a responsibility which non-land-owning sportsmen may encourage, but cannot carry.

It is worth repeating that "hunting quail is not a fundamental right of sportsmen. It is a privilege." The granting of this privilege rests beyond question with the landowner, the producer.

Throughout the recent expressions of our leading conservationists, the same theme is repeated often: "Food and cover—habitat for bobwhites—private-land management." These are the essential elements to expand conservation and restoration. Let those who wish entertain themselves by raising a few birds in captivity. Allow others to remain buried complacently in their ancient cherished traditions. But to those who want bobwhites enough to work intelligently and progressively, the reward lies in "land management."

BIBLIOGRAPHY

The life habits and management of the bobwhite have been covered in many articles by many authors. Much of the information is sketchy, in the nature of progress reports, or of local character only. Many ideas are out-of-date and are so recognized by the same authors in later publications. The following bibliography lists the more important publications on the subject.

Allen, Durward L. 1938. Some observations on fall and winter food patches for birds in southern Michigan. Wilson Bul. (Sioux City, Iowa 60¢) 50 (1), pp. 42–46.
——. 1941. Relationships of winter weather to farmland wildlife in the midwest. Proceedings Central Snow Conf., Vol. 1, pp. 95–102.
Bennitt, Rudolph. 1937. An inquiry: "Development and maintenance of food and cover—where and by whom?" Trans. Second N.A.W.C., pp. 264–267.
Bickford, C. A., and L. S. Newcomb. 1947. Instructions for:

"Prescribed burning in the Florida Flatwoods." Fire Control Notes. Forest Service U.S.D.A. Vol. 8, No. 1, pp. 17–24.

Bode, I. T. 1938. Trans. Third N.A.W.C., pp. 20–22. Comments on "How best to plant for wildlife in land management."

Copley, T. L. et al. 1944. Investigations in Erosion Control. U.S.D.A. Tech. Bul. No. 873, 66 pp. Supt. of Documents, Washington, D. C.

Davison, Verne E. 1941. Wildlife borders—an innovation in farm management. Jour. Wild. Mgt., 4: 390–394.

——. 1942 a. Thirty million acres of undiscovered wildlife-land in the U. S. Trans. Seventh N.A.W.C., pp. 366–375.

——. 1942 b. Bobwhite foods and conservation farming. Jour. Wild. Mgt., 6: 97–109.

——. 1945. Wildlife values of the lespedezas. Jour. Wild. Mgt. 9: 1–9.

——. 1948. Bicolor lespedeza—for quail and soil conservation in the Southeast. U.S.D.A. Leaflet No. 248. 8 pp. illus.

Edminster, F. C. and J. R. Langenback. 1944. Food for thought —and wildlife. Pa. Game News., Jan. A report on feeding experiments.

Errington, Paul L. 1936. Differences in nutritive values of winter game foods. Trans. First N.A.W.C., pp. 356–360.

——. 1946. Predation and vertebrate populations. Quarterly Rev. of Biol., Vol. 21 (2), pp. 161–163. A thorough review of the literature on predation.

Fry, John R. 1938. Wildlife food patches: results of 4 years of observations in southwestern Wisc. Trans. Third N.A.W.C., pp. 730–735.

Gerstell, Richard. 1942. The place of winter feeding in practical game management. Bul. 3, Pa. Game Comm., 121 pp.

Gordon, Seth. 1938. Trans. Third N.A.W.C., pp. 22–29. Comments on: How best to plan for wildlife in land management.

Graham, Edw. H. 1947. The land and wildlife. Oxford Press.

Grenne, S. W. 1935. Effect of annual grass fires on organic matter . . . of virgin longleaf pine soils. U. S. Gov't. printing office.

Hawkins, Arthur S. 1937. Winter feeding at Faville Grove, Wisc., 1935-37, Jour. Wild. Mgt. 1 (3–4), pp. 62–69.

Lay, Daniel W. 1940. Bobwhite populations as affected by woodland management in eastern Texas. Tex. Agr. Exp. Sta., Bul. 592, 37 pp.

Leopold, Aldo. 1931. Game survey of the north central states, 300 p.

——. 1933. Game management, Scribner's.

——. 1937. A plea for "research program". Trans. Second N.A.W.C., pp. 104–107.

——. 1938. Wildlife research . . . Trans. Third N.A.W.C., pp. 42–45. A critical discussion of wildlife research.

——. 1939. Farmer-Sportsman. Trans. Fourth N.A.W.C., pp. 144–175. A discussion of farmer-sportsmen problems.

——. 1940. Wisconsin Wildlife Chronology. Wisc. Cons. Bul. V (II).

——. 1945. The outlook for farm wildlife. Trans. Tenth N.A.W.C., pp. 165–168.

Miller, J. Paul, and B. B. Powell. 1942. Game production on agricultural land. U.S.D.A. Circ. 636. 58 pp. A revealing report on the importance of private lands to wildlife management.

Nestler, R. B. 1946. Mechanical value of grit for bobwhite quail. Jour. Wild. Mgt. 10 (2), pp. 137–142.

——. 1949. Acceptance of seeds of four legumes by the bobwhite quail. Jour. Wild. Mgt. 13 (1), pp. 143–144.

Nestler, R. B., and W. W. Bailey. 1943. Vitamin A deficiency in bobwhite quail. Jour. Wild. Mgt. 7 (2), pp. 170–173.

Nestler, R. B. et al. 1944. Winter protein requirements of bobwhite quail. Jour. Wild. Mgt. 8 (3), pp. 218–220.

Steavenson, Hugh A. 1946. Multiflora rose for farm hedges. Jour. Wild. Mgt. 10 (3), pp. 227–234.

Stoddard, Herbert L. 1931. The bobwhite quail. Scribner's Sons, N. Y., pp. 559.

——. 1939. Use of Controlled fire in southeastern game management, Coop. Quail Study Assn., 21 pp.

Stoddard, Herbert L., and E. V. Komarek, 1941 a. The carrying capacity of southeastern quail lands. Trans. Sixth N.A.W.C., pp. 148–155.

Watson, C. W. 1944. A cooperative approach to farm game management, Trans. Ninth N.A.W.C., pp. 304–308.

Wood, George W. 1939. Farmer-Sportsman. Trans. Fourth N.A.W.C., pp. 149–152. A discussion of farmer-sportsman problems.